Macmillan/McGraw-Hill Science

Air, WEATHER and Climate

AUTHORS

Mary Atwater
The University of Georgia

Prentice Baptiste
University of Houston

Lucy Daniel
Spindale Schools; Rutherfordton, NC

Jay Hackett
University of Northern Colorado

Richard Moyer
University of Michigan, Dearborn

Carol Takemoto
Los Angeles Unified School District

Nancy Wilson
Sacramento Unified School District

*Fog in the mountains of
Kalalau Valley on the
Na Pali Coast in Kauai, Hawaii*

Macmillan/McGraw-Hill
School Publishing Company
New York   Chicago   Columbus

MACMILLAN / McGRAW-HILL

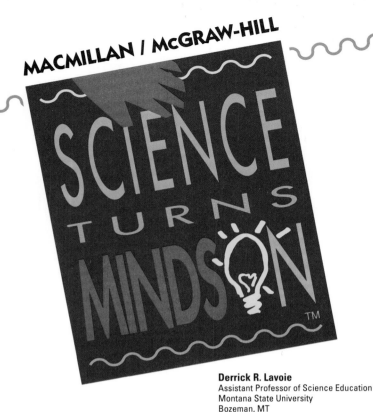

Derrick R. Lavoie
Assistant Professor of Science Education
Montana State University
Bozeman, MT

CONSULTANTS

Assessment:
Mary Hamm
Associate Professor
Department of Elementary Education
San Francisco State University
San Francisco, CA

Cognitive Development:
Pat Guild, Ed.D.
Director, Graduate Programs in Education and
Learning Styles Consultant
Antioch University
Seattle, WA

Kathi Hand, M.A.Ed.
Middle School Teacher and Learning Styles Consultant
Assumption School
Seattle, WA

Cooperative Learning:
Marcia Batcheller Harter
Director, Curriculum and Staff Development
Assistant Superintendent, Educational Services
Monterey County Office of Education
Salinas, CA

Earth Science:
David G. Futch
Associate Professor of Biology
San Diego State University
San Diego, CA

Dr. Shadia Rifai Habbal
Harvard-Smithsonian Center for Astrophysics
Cambridge, MA

Dr. Tom Murphree
Department of Meteorology, Naval Postgraduate
School
Monterey, CA

Suzanne O'Connell
Assistant Professor
Wesleyan University
Middletown, CT

Sidney E. White
Professor of Geology
The Ohio State University
Columbus, OH

Environmental Education:
Cheryl Charles, Ph.D.
Executive Director
Project Wild
Boulder, CO

Gifted:
Dr. James A. Curry
Associate Professor, Graduate Faculty
College of Education, University of Southern Maine
Gorham, ME

Global Education:
M. Eugene Gilliom
Professor of Social Studies and Global Education
The Ohio State University
Columbus, OH

Life Science:
Wyatt W. Anderson
Professor of Genetics
University of Georgia
Athens, GA

Orin G. Gelderloos
Professor of Biology and Professor of Environmental Studies
University of Michigan—Dearborn
Dearborn, MI

Donald C. Lisowy
Education Specialist
New York, NY

Dr. E.K. Merrill
Assistant Professor
University of Wisconsin Center—Rock County
Madison, WI

Literature:
Dr. Donna E. Norton
Texas A&M University
College Station, TX

Macmillan/McGraw-Hill School Division
10 Union Square East
New York, New York 10003
Printed in the United States of America

ISBN 0-02-274277-8 / 6

1 2 3 4 5 6 7 8 9 RRW 99 98 97 96 95 94 93 92

Mathematics:
Dr. Richard Lodholz
Parkway School
St. Louis, MO

Middle School Specialist:
Daniel Rodriguez
Principal
Pomona, CA

Misconceptions:
Dr. Charles W. Anderson
Michigan State University
East Lansing, MI

Dr. Edward L. Smith
Michigan State University
East Lansing, MI

Multicultural:
Bernard L. Charles
Senior Vice President
Quality Education for Minorities Network
Washington, DC

Paul B. Janeczko
Poet
Hebron, MA

James R. Murphy
Math Teacher
La Guardia High School
New York, NY

Clifford E. Trafzer
Professor and Chair, Ethnic Studies
University of California, Riverside
Riverside, CA

Physical Science:
Gretchen M. Gillis
Geologist
Maxus Exploration Company
Dallas, TX

Henry C. McBay
Professor of Chemistry
Morehouse College and Clark Atlanta University
Atlanta, GA

Wendell H. Potter
Associate Professor of Physics
Department of Physics
University of California, Davis
Davis, CA

Claudia K. Viehland
Educational Consultant, Chemist
Sigma Chemical Company
St. Louis, MO

Reading:
Charles Temple, Ph.D.
Associate Professor of Education
Hobart and William Smith Colleges
Geneva, NY

Safety:
Janice Sutkus
Program Manager: Education
National Safety Council
Chicago, IL

Science Technology and Society (STS):
William C. Kyle, Jr.
Director, School Mathematics and Science Center
Purdue University
West Lafayette, IN

Social Studies:
Jean Craven
District Coordinator of Curriculum Development
Albuquerque Public Schools
Albuquerque, NM

Special Needs:
Paulette J. Thomas, Ph.D.
Professor of Special Education
University of New Orleans
New Orleans, LA

Students Acquiring English:
Mario Ruiz
Pomona, CA

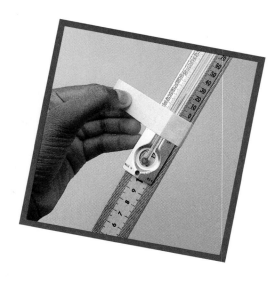

STUDENT ACTIVITY TESTERS

Alveria Henderson	Andrew Duffy
Kate McGlumphy	Chris Higgins
Katherine Petzinger	Sean Pruitt
John Wirtz	Joanna Huber
Sarah Wittenbrink	John Petzinger

FIELD TEST TEACHERS

Kathy Bowles
Landmark Middle School
Jacksonville, FL

Myra Dietz
#46 School
Rochester, NY

John Gridley
H.L. Harshman Junior High School #101
Indianapolis, IN

Annette Porter
Schenk Middle School
Madison, WI

Connie Boone
Fletcher Middle School
Jacksonville, FL

Theresa Smith
Bates Middle School
Annapolis, MD

Debbie Stamler
Margaret Tierney
Sennett Middle School
Madison, WI

CONTRIBUTING WRITER

Barbara Keeler

ACKNOWLEDGEMENTS

Reprinted with the permission of Macmillan Publishing Company from *RAINBOWS MIRAGES AND SUNDOGS: The Sky as a Source of Wonder* by Roy A. Gallant. Copyright © 1987 by Roy A. Gallant.

Excerpt from *NIGHT OF THE TWISTERS* by Ivy Ruckman. Copyright © 1984 by Ivy Ruckman. Reprinted by permission of HarperCollins Publishers.

Air, Weather, & Climate

Activities!

EXPLORE

TRY THIS

Features

Links

Literature Link

Language Arts Link

Math Link

Social Studies Link

Health Link

CAREERS

SCIENCE TECHNOLOGY and Society

Focus on Technology

Departments

Air, Weather, & Climate

Volcanic ash

hen you look up on a clear day, what do you see? You're looking up through hundreds of kilometers of atmosphere. Humans and most other living organisms live in a vast ocean of air. Like the Pacific Ocean, the air contains many living creatures. Birds sail overhead, insects buzz in your ears or hover over flowers, and seeds are carried by the wind. You may not think about the atmosphere very often, but you're aware of the changes that take place in it. The atmosphere is responsible for breathtaking sunsets, rainbows, frost on your windows, and dew on the grass. It also keeps you alive. People can survive for weeks without food and for days without water. But without air, they die in a few minutes. Every day you breathe about 23,000 liters (about 6,000 gallons) of air!

Most planets have atmospheres, including Earth. If

Stormfront

Snowflake

Alpine climate

there were no atmosphere at all, you would burn to a crisp in the daytime and freeze at night. But just having an atmosphere doesn't mean that a planet can support life. Mars has an atmosphere, but it wouldn't keep you alive. You need certain substances in the air you breathe. A slight change in the atmosphere would make Earth unlivable for many forms of life.

Earth's atmosphere contains volcanic ash, alpine climates, snow, and storms.

Rainbow

Rain puddles

The atmosphere is the place where all weather takes place. The atmosphere also controls all changes in weather. In this unit, you'll learn about how weather affects people's lives. You'll also learn which types of weather patterns are changed by human activity.

Minds On! As you explore this unit, observe the weather each day. On *Activity Log* page 1, write down what you observe on the first day. After that, fill a notebook with your Weather-watch data allowing about a half page for each day.

Is the day hot, cold, warm, or cool? Is it raining or snowing? Are the skies clear, cloudy, or partly cloudy? Is the air clean? Is it windy? Is the wind strong or light? Does the weather seem about to change? What makes you think so? As you learn more about the atmosphere and weather, you'll begin to record additional information.

Dry land

Snow at Grand Canyon

Each day after you note your weather-watch data, summarize your activities for that day, especially if they were influenced by the weather. Describe what you wore. When you've finished this unit, you'll understand much more about the weather conditions you observed. Most importantly, you'll have some ideas about what you can do to help protect one of our most important resources—our atmosphere. ●

Rainbows, rain, scorching heat and snow are all caused by changes in Earth's atmosphere.

Science in Literature

What makes the sky change? What causes the weather? What do different ent sky pictures mean? Anyone who has ever looked into the sky and asked questions like these is ready to understand how air, weather, and climate act together above our heads to produce special effects. In the nonfiction books described here, learn how patterns in the sky mark coming changes. In the fiction books, experience terror and delight with the characters as they, too, learn how the sky systems work.

Night of the Twisters by Ivy Ruckman.

New York: Thomas Y. Crowell, 1984.

Have you ever seen a tornado? The three teenagers in this novel lived through a string of seven tornadoes that destroyed most of their Nebraska town late one summer evening. Read it to learn how people respond to terror and to disaster. How do you think you'd react if a roaring windstorm threatened to carry off your pets, your neighbors, your family, or yourself? Even if you lived through it, could you ever be the same? How would your town and the lives of everyone in it be changed? And could you ever enjoy a beautiful, boisterous thunderstorm again?

Rainbows, Mirages, and Sundogs: The Sky as a Source of Wonder by Roy A. Gallant.

New York: Macmillan, 1987.

Have you ever seen a ring around the sun? The northern lights? A mother-of-pearl cloud? These and many other mysteries of the skies appear in this, another of Roy Gallant's carefully crafted books. Excellent black-and-white photographs and clear diagrams help to explain the causes and frequencies of odd weather phenomena such as eclipses, star trails, clouds with silver linings, and the ghostly light of the zodiac.

Other Good Books To Read

Tornado! by Hilary Milton. New York: Franklin Watts, 1983.

This novel is about a fourteen-year-old boy who saves his family's life. Imagine a flooded road and a washed-out bridge, a seven-year-old sister bitten by a copperhead snake, a mom with a broken ankle, and, to top it all off, two tornadoes. Paul is definitely the man of the hour.

Simple Weather Experiments With Everyday Materials by Muriel Mandell. New York: Sterling Publishing Co., 1990.

Have you ever cut a hailstone? Made a sundial? Made an indoor cloud? These are just some of the experiments you can do with this book. Best of all, it explains the science behind each mystery.

It's Raining Cats and Dogs by Franklyn M. Branley. Boston: Houghton Mifflin, 1987.

Facts, folklore, science experiments, and memorable weather fill this book with interest. Have you ever measured the size of raindrops? Do you know how cities make their own climate? Read this book!

Earth is surrounded by an atmosphere of air that you breathe every day. Have you ever wondered about the air? Is air everywhere? What's it like far above Earth? In this lesson, you'll discover what makes up the atmosphere and why Earth needs one.

Hot-air balloons take passengers high into the atmosphere.

What's the Nature of Earth's Atmosphere?

Ancient peoples knew that air existed. Looking up through the atmosphere that surrounds Earth, these early scientists asked many questions—How high does the atmosphere extend? Is the air in the upper atmosphere different from the air near the ground? After hot-air balloons were invented in 1783, scientists used them to travel far above Earth's surface, searching for answers to their questions.

Minds On! Imagine you're taking a ride in a hot-air balloon. The balloon will rise until you're as high as the top of Mount Kilimanjaro in northern Tanzania—almost 6,000 meters (a bit less than 20,000 feet) above sea level. How will the air change as you rise? You have with you a thermometer. Predict what will happen to the temperature as the balloon climbs higher. On **Activity Log** page 2, write and explain your predictions. ●

Before hot-air balloons were invented, some curious scientists climbed mountains to study air at greater heights. Suppose you were going to climb Mount Kilimanjaro. What would the air be like as you climbed that high? Would the air be warmer or cooler than the air at Earth's surface?

Activity!

Has the Temperature of Earth Changed Over Time?

People have often wondered if Earth has become warmer or if it's become cooler with the passage of time. In this activity, you'll make a model to see how the temperature of Earth is affected by day and night.

What You Need

1-L bottle
plastic cup
sand
cotton balls
thermometer
watch with second hand
water
funnel
metric ruler
Activity Log pages 3–4

What To Do

1 Place the funnel into the opening of the 1-L bottle and pour 2 c of sand into the plastic bottle. Slowly add water until the sand is soaked. Think of the bottle system as a model planet Earth.

2 Place the thermometer into the bottle until the bulb is about 10 cm above the sand. Wedge cotton balls in the bottle-neck to keep the thermometer in place.

3 Set the model Earth outside in the shade until its inside temperature hasn't changed for 10 mins. Record this temperature in your *Activity Log* and label it STARTING TEMPERATURE.

4 Set the model Earth in the sun and record the inside temperature every min for 10 mins. Quickly move the bottle to the shade, and record the temperature each min for 10 more mins. Label the last reading ENDING TEMPERATURE.

5 Plot the time and temperature data on graphs—1 graph for the shade, another for the sun.

What Happened?

1. The time that your model Earth spent in the sun represents daytime. Describe what happened to the temperature of the model Earth's atmosphere during the "day."

2. What happened to the temperature at "night"—the period it was in the shade?

3. Compare the beginning and ending temperatures. What can you conclude about the amount of energy received and the amount lost during this model of day and night?

What Now?

1. Suppose that over a long period of time, Earth received more energy than it sent back into space. What would happen to the overall temperatures within Earth's atmosphere?

2. What would happen if Earth gave off more energy than it received?

3. Scientists refer to Earth's energy gain and loss as a budget. You could compare it to a money budget. Pretend you have $25.00 in a bank account and each week you receive an allowance of $5.00. The allowance you receive each week is income. The money you spend each week is your outgo. What happens to your account if you spend less each week than you receive? What happens if you spend more each week than you receive? How is a money budget like Earth's energy budget?

4. Now think about Earth again. Suppose Earth were closer to the sun than it really is. How would this affect daytime temperatures of the atmosphere? What would have to happen for Earth to maintain an energy balance?

15

The Atmosphere

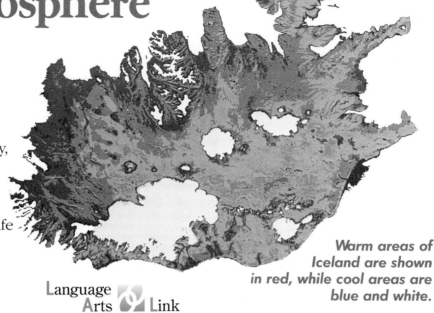

Warm areas of Iceland are shown in red, while cool areas are blue and white.

In the Explore Activity, you discovered that Earth maintains an energy balance. One of the factors that makes life possible on Earth is its distance from the sun. If Earth were just a little closer to or farther from the sun, you couldn't live on Earth. The other planets in the solar system are much too cold or too hot to support life as we know it. Earth is heated by the energy in the sun's rays. We receive this energy from the sun in the form of **solar radiation** or energy released by the sun.

The Cherokee people have a story that describes how Earth once received varying amounts of energy from the sun. First it was thought that Earth was too close to the sun, the story says, and then it moved too far from the sun. Finally, it reached a distance on which all the beings on Earth could agree, and there it remained.

Language Arts Link

A "Sun"sational Story!

In your library, search for myths, folklore, and fairy tales about the sun. Select at least one that demonstrates people's understanding of the sun's importance as the source of all energy and the sun's influence on life.

Your teacher or librarian can assist you if needed. Share your story with the class and explain how the story shows the author's understanding of the sun's importance.

Cold conditions in Norway cause glaciers to form.

Some of the solar radiation entering Earth's atmosphere never reaches the ground. Some of it's reflected back into space by the tops of clouds, and some is scattered by dust particles in the atmosphere. Earth's surface also reflects some of the sun's energy back into space. The rest of the energy is absorbed by the atmosphere and clouds and by the planet's surface. As Earth absorbs energy, it becomes warm.

You may have noticed that rock and paved streets are cold in the morning and become warmer towards afternoon. Perhaps you've seen snakes and other animals warming themselves on sunny rocks.

The energy from the sun is absorbed by the atmosphere and by Earth. Earth eventually radiates the energy back to space in the form of **infrared rays**—or rays of energy that, when absorbed by an object, warm the object. Thus, Earth maintains a **radiation balance** by receiving and releasing an equal amount of energy.

You learned in the Explore Activity on pages 14 and 15 that the sand in your plastic bottle lost the same amount of energy as it gained. Earth loses and gains the same amount of energy over great spans of time. In other words, over hundreds of millions of years, Earth has neither warmed up nor cooled down. There were periods of time, though, when Earth was cooler, and vast sheets of ice covered much of its surface. At other times, it was slightly warmer, and instead of ice, oceans covered much of North America and other continents. Overall, however, Earth has maintained an energy balance.

Certain gases in the atmosphere allow the sun's energy to reach Earth but prevent or slow its escape into space. Scientists fear that some of these gases won't allow heat to escape from Earth. Thus, Earth may become warmer over a period of time. This is a theory known as the greenhouse effect.

Animals can absorb warmth from heated rocks.

17

Warmer temperatures on Earth could cause much damage. Warming of Earth could cause glaciers and polar ice caps to melt. That would free enough water to flood much of Earth's land. If Earth warmed a few degrees, melting glaciers could raise the ocean enough to cover coastal and bay areas. If the ocean rises as much as 6 meters (about 20 feet), it would be a disaster for coastal cities, most of which are only 3 meters (about 10 feet) above sea level. Cities such as Venice, Italy would be overcome by water because their damming systems couldn't hold it. Coastal areas of Africa would be under water, New York City's sewage plants would be flooded, and Bermuda might vanish. Even with a rise of just 1 meter (about 3 feet) in ocean depth, tens of millions of people could be affected when their drinking water supplies became polluted.

Remember that the greenhouse effect is a theory. However, the near future will tell how realistic it is. To see how you can test the theory, do the Try This Activity.

Icebergs are found in polar regions. They contain fresh water.

Activity!

How High Will the Water Rise?

What You Need

9 oz cup
3 to 5 large ice cubes
pen or marker with waterproof ink
small rock
Activity Log page 5

Add water to the cup until it's 3 cm (about 1 in.) deep. Place the rock in the water. Take it out and mark it to show how much of it was under water. Make your mark on the dry part just above the water line. Put the rock back into the cup. Add ice to the cup. When the ice cubes have melted, notice how much of the rock is under water. How much higher is the water line on the rock? In your **Activity Log**, answer this question—What would happen to islands and continents if the polar ice caps melted?

Earth's atmosphere is made up of several layers. The energy absorbed by Earth warms the atmosphere above it. Temperatures in the atmosphere vary according to altitude.

The **exosphere** is a layer within the thermosphere. This layer extends into space. The temperature rises and continues to rise until it reaches several thousand degrees.

The **thermosphere** is the highest layer of the atmosphere. It begins just above the mesosphere and extends into space.

In this middle layer, the **mesosphere,** the temperature begins to decrease again. This layer is the coldest layer of the atmosphere.

The **stratosphere** is the layer of the atmosphere that contains an ozone layer. The temperature rises because the ozone absorbs the sun's energy.

The **troposphere** is the lowest layer of Earth's atmosphere. This is where our weather takes place. The temperature of the air continues to drop the higher you go.

The atmosphere seems very thick, but compared to Earth's diameter, the entire atmosphere is quite thin. If you made a scale model of Earth with the planet about the size of an apple, its entire atmosphere would be about as thick as the apple peel. The troposphere would be very thin indeed. Although the troposphere is thin compared to the outer layers of the atmosphere, it contains most of the gases in the atmosphere because of the force of gravity.

How do we know that air exists? You can't see it unless it's dirty. Unless it's hot, cold, wet, or moving, you can't feel it. People often forget about air. If you poured all the juice out of a can, it would be full of air. Yet if you asked someone what was in the can, the person would probably say, "Nothing. It's empty." He or she would be wrong, of course. To prove for yourself that air exists, do the Try This Activity.

Winds carry particles that allow people to see how air moves.

TRY THIS Activity!

Prove Air Is Real

One of the first people to demonstrate the existence of air was a Greek named Hero. You can do the same.

What You Need
cup, bucket or sink, water, *Activity Log* page 6

Turn the cup upside down and quickly push it straight down into a bucket or sink full of water until the rim of the cup touches the bottom. Continue holding the cup against the bottom and don't let the cup tip. Is there any water in the cup? Why? Now tip the cup and let some of the trapped air escape. After you see the bubbles of air shoot to the surface, what do you observe? Write what you've observed in your *Activity Log.*

What Is Air?

Volcanoes like Mt. St. Helens continue to add gases to Earth's atmosphere.

Now you've proved that air exists, but what is it? The air in Earth's atmosphere contains a mixture of gases, liquids, and solids. Scientists theorize that the atmosphere began to form when Earth itself was first forming. Gases escaped from Earth's interior through volcanoes like the one pictured on this page, and other openings in Earth's newly formed crust. By studying gases volcanoes release today, scientists can speculate about what gases early volcanoes may have released. They theorize that Earth releases the same gases from its interior today as it did then. These gases include water vapor, carbon dioxide, nitrogen, ammonia, and methane. The newly formed atmosphere contained about ten percent carbon dioxide and no oxygen. Life as we know it couldn't have survived in this early atmosphere.

However, the atmosphere changed over time. Since hydrogen has a smaller mass, hydrogen molecules rose high into the upper atmosphere. Rain washed most of the carbon dioxide from the atmosphere into the oceans and onto the land. There the carbon combined with other elements to form compounds such as methane. Methane reacts to form other gases or combines with other substances. With most of the water vapor and carbon dioxide gone from the atmosphere, nitrogen soon came to make up 78 percent of the air near Earth's surface. That is still true today.

Focus on Technology

Fuel From the Air?

Today, scientists use electricity to break down water into hydrogen and oxygen. The process, called electrolysis, could be important in the future.

You've probably heard that if the world's people keep using oil at the present rate, supplies will run out. One kind of fuel that can be used to replace oil is hydrogen, a product of electrolysis. Of all known fuels, it is the most pollution-free when burned. Burning hydrogen gives off only water vapor and traces of nitrogen.

Hydrogen is already being used to power automobiles. In Germany, some car manufacturers began testing hydrogen-powered cars in the late 1980s. Experimental buses powered by hydrogen operated for a short time in Provo, Utah, and Riverside, California.

However, hydrogen as a fuel does have some serious disadvantages. It's highly flammable and explosive. Because it's lighter than air, it was used in the 1930s to keep zeppelins aloft. Zeppelins resembled huge blimps. Their use was discontinued in 1937 after a German zeppelin, the *Hindenburg,* burst into flames, sending many passengers to a fiery death. Researchers are finding safer ways to transport and store hydrogen.

Hydrogen can even be used to power automobiles.

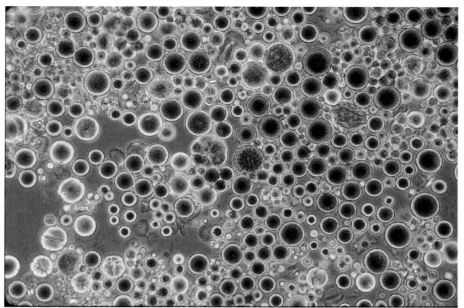
Cyanobacteria were the earliest forms of life. They made food from the sun's energy.

Oxygen, the other product of electrolysis, wouldn't remain in the air on most planets. It combines easily and quickly with other elements to form compounds such as iron oxide, or rust, and carbon dioxide. On Earth, plants continually renew the supply of oxygen. In making food, the plants took in carbon dioxide, which is made of carbon and oxygen. Organisms, such as cyanobacteria, used the carbon and some of the oxygen and gave off the leftover oxygen as a waste product. Over time, the oxygen content of the air increased. Earth's present atmosphere is 78 percent nitrogen and 21 percent oxygen. The remaining one percent of air is made up of tiny amounts of other gases, including carbon dioxide and water vapor.

Today, plants continue to use carbon dioxide and oxygen. People and other animals breathe in oxygen and give off carbon dioxide. It sounds quite stable, doesn't it? Well, until quite recently, Earth's atmosphere hadn't changed much for two million years. But since the Industrial Revolution, which took place in the 19th century, large quantities of smoke and other pollutants have been added to the air. From about 1850 to the present, Earth's atmosphere has changed relatively rapidly.

Oxygen and hydrogen aren't the only gases in the atmosphere. The most abundant gas is nitrogen. It makes life possible on Earth. Bacteria draw nitrogen into the soil, where the nitrogen is used as a nutrient for plants.

Minds On!
Labels on food products have lists of ingredients or contents. Some people like to know the ingredients in the foods they eat. Yet, even though humans take in ten times as much air daily as they do food, some people don't know or care about what the air contains. Suppose you needed to make a label showing people what they breathe. What would you put on a list of the contents of Earth's atmosphere? Make a creative label for the composition of the atmosphere and draw it in your *Activity Log* on page 7. ●

> INGREDIENTS:
> Raisins,
> Almonds,
> Peanuts, Soy
> Nuts, Sunflower
> Seeds, Walnuts,
> Vegetable Oil or
> Peanut Oil.

The ingredients of food products are listed on labels.

Improving Earth's Atmosphere

People are trying to protect our atmosphere and the quality of the air we breathe. One such group of people who help are the TREE MUSKETEERS.

TREE MUSKETEERS is a nonprofit corporation staffed and run by members from 10 to 18 years of age. The group was started in 1987 by 13 Brownies in El Segundo, California. They were concerned about air pollution, the hole in the ozone layer, disappearing forests, and environmental damage. They decided not to point fingers of blame or push other people to do things, but to take action themselves. Since then, the group has grown to 300 members and has planted 620 trees in their community. They established the first complete recycling center in El Segundo. The members publish a regular environmental-education column in the local newspaper, and they persuade local merchants to carry products that don't cause pollution. They produce and broadcast a television

Planting trees is one duty of the TREE MUSKETEERS.

quiz show about the environment. They've set up a speaker's bureau to address youth and adult groups around the country about the environment. TREE MUSKETEERS now has a nationwide environmental

hotline. Their example inspired local businesses and residents to take their own steps on behalf of the environment.

Awards and commendations cover the walls of their headquarters. The group won the 1988 National President's Environmental Youth Award, presented by the Environmental Protection Agency. They also won a Creative Project Award from the Los Angeles Girl Scout Council. They're especially proud of a National Arbor Day Foundation award, because they competed with adults to win it. TREE MUSKETEERS was also awarded a Certificate of Appreciation for Outstanding Conservation Endeavors. In addition, they have many awards from state and local government agencies.

The TREE MUSKETEERS wish to expand their membership. Future projects are to continue to plant trees, and to meet with people of the business community and government agencies to inspire them to support environmental issues. Their ultimate goal is to influence the lives of other people and help them to become environmentally aware of their actions.

Minds On! Suppose you were starting a group to help reduce air pollution and greenhouse gases. What steps could the group take? Who could help? Imagine you and the group have been asked to do a public service commercial for television. Its purpose is to get people to do something that will improve air quality. Meet in groups of four, plan your commercial, and present it to the class. ●

Sum It Up

You've learned that Earth receives its energy from the sun. Over time, the solar radiation that reaches Earth is reflected or radiated back into space, as you demonstrated with your model Earth. If this weren't so, then the temperature of Earth would increase until life as we know it couldn't exist. If Earth's atmosphere is warming, as some studies indicate, we need to be aware of how and why in order to either adapt to the changes or reverse them. As you become familiar with the ocean of air in which you live, your understanding of how it interacts with Earth will become more complete. The top layers interact with those on the bottom; the gases in one place affect life in another; solar energy absorbed is radiated away into space. In the next lessons, you'll see how winds and other weather patterns help to keep this soup kettle we call our atmosphere well stirred.

Critical Thinking

1. One greenhouse gas is carbon dioxide. What can be done to reduce carbon dioxide levels in the atmosphere?
2. Why does the temperature of Earth's lower atmosphere decrease with altitude?
3. Why does the air temperature in the upper atmosphere or thermosphere reach 1,000°C?
4. What can we learn about Earth's interior by studying Earth's atmosphere? Hint: Think about volcanoes.
5. Why is nitrogen so much more abundant in the present atmosphere than oxygen or hydrogen?

Why Do Daily Temperatures and Pressures Change?

How does the weather affect you and what you do? How can changes in temperature and air pressure cause winds to strengthen or die down? What are the patterns of weather around the world, and how can they be predicted? In this lesson, you'll explore some of the same things scientists explore when they try to answer these questions.

Temperatures in deserts range from extremely hot during the day to very cool at night.

You've discovered that Earth's surface absorbs more of the sun's radiation than the atmosphere does. When you've walked barefoot on a hot day, you've probably noticed how much energy the ground absorbed.

Where would you walk to avoid getting your feet burned—a cement sidewalk, a lawn, a sandy stretch of beach, or a black asphalt street? If you were swimming in a lake or river on a hot day, which would be warmer, the water or the land away from the water?

You may have noticed that the sun feels hotter on your skin at certain times of the day. During what part of the day is a person most likely to sunburn? Why? Why is one place warmer than another?

Why does the wind blow? You may have watched the wind sweep across a field, sending ripples through the grass. Perhaps you've also watched it swish through a park or forest, rustling the leaves. Have you ever wondered what causes wind? Ancient people wondered, and some developed hypotheses to explain it. One such explanation was that wind was the breath from different kinds of plants. By the end of this lesson, you'll be able to describe wind scientifically.

Activity!

You're Getting Warmer

In this activity, you'll explore some factors affecting air temperature outside your own school building. Outside your school on a hot afternoon, where should it be warmest? Coolest?

What You Need

meterstick
thermometer
masking tape
watch with second hand
Activity Log pages 8–9

What To Do

1 Draw an aerial view of your school in your *Activity Log.*

2 Go outside and select at least 8 sites around the building. Mark these sites on your aerial drawing. Make sure at least 3 locations are sunny and have different types of surfaces such as grass, soil, cement, or asphalt.

3 Predict which sites will be warmest and which will be coolest. Write reasons for your predictions in your *Activity Log.*

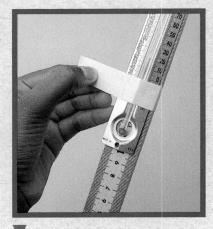

4 Tape the thermometer to the meter stick so its bulb is 10 cm from the bottom.

5 Measure and record the air temperature 10 cm above the ground at each site with the stick straight up. Make sure that the sun is not shining on the thermometer. Wait for 2 mins at each site before you read the temperature. Record the data in your *Activity Log*.

What Happened?

1. Which general area around the building was warmest? Which area was coolest?
2. Which individual site was hottest? What type of surface was at this site?
3. Which site was coolest? What was its surface?
4. How do these results compare with your predictions?

What Now?

1. How does the ground surface affect afternoon air temperatures?
2. At what time of day is the outside air temperature warmest? Explain why.
3. Using what you've learned, which classrooms in your building are the warmest during the afternoon? Without air-conditioning, what could be done to help keep these rooms cooler?

Energy Received by Earth

Alaska

Algeria

 hy is Algeria hotter than Alaska? By measuring temperatures around your school building, you discovered that Earth isn't warmed evenly. Why do you think these variations occur? To investigate one possible reason, do the activity on the following page.

Earth has many different temperature variations. The locations of land masses on Earth determine what the temperature will be.

Rays that strike at a steep angle are spread over a smaller area than rays that strike Earth at a shallow angle.

TRY THIS

Activity!

Light Up a World

Can you explain the fact that Earth's surface isn't evenly warmed?

What You Need
world globe
flashlight
***Activity Log* page 10**

Darken the room. Shine the flashlight on the globe, pointing it at the equator. What parts of the world are in the brightest light? The dimmest light? Write your observations in your *Activity Log.* How does this model explain why the North and South Poles have colder temperatures?

As you discovered in the activity, when the sun is high in the sky, the sun's rays strike Earth at a steeper angle than when the sun is low in the sky. In low latitudes, the sun is high in the sky during the middle of summer. These areas tend to be the warmest places. The angle of the sun's rays also explains why people need to avoid the sun at noon. In most locations, the sun is more directly over-head then, and the rays are stronger.

Even within one city, temperatures may vary dramatically. During part of the year, a city warms in the sun, and its residents struggle to stay cool. A few months later, blizzards bury it in snow. This happens in a given location because the angle of the sun changes in the course of a year.

Earth is tilted on its axis. Therefore, as it revolves around the sun, different parts of Earth receive the sun's rays at right angles. The sun's rays fall most directly within the tropical zones north and south of the equator. In the areas north of the Tropic of Cancer and south of the Tropic of Capricorn, the sun's rays are never directly overhead.

Can you explain why places at high elevations, even those near the equator, are cold? For example, find Mount Kilimanjaro on a map. Notice that it is in the tropics. Can you explain why it has snow near its peak?

In the temperate zones, the change in the angle at which the sun strikes Earth from winter to summer is very significant. As the angle of the sun changes, so do the seasons. Hours of daylight increase or decrease. Summers are warm or hot, and winters are cool or cold. Most of Earth's people live in the temperate zones.

During the summer, the polar zones receive 24 hours of daylight. In the winter, these zones are dark for 24 hours. For example, the North Pole has continuous daylight for 189 days starting June 22, but beginning December 22, the North Pole is completely dark for 176 days.

Areas within your community are also warmed unevenly. At this moment, if the sun is shining, different surfaces are absorbing different amounts of the sun's energy. Dark-colored surfaces, such as black asphalt

*Earth has three major climate zones. **Climate** is an average of all weather conditions of an area over a long period of time, such as 100 years. The weather conditions of an area depend upon which climate zone an area is located.*

*North and south of the tropics, between the latitudes of about 30 and 60 degrees, lie the temperate (tem´prit) zones. **Temperate** means "mild or moderate in temperature," and that describes the climate there.*

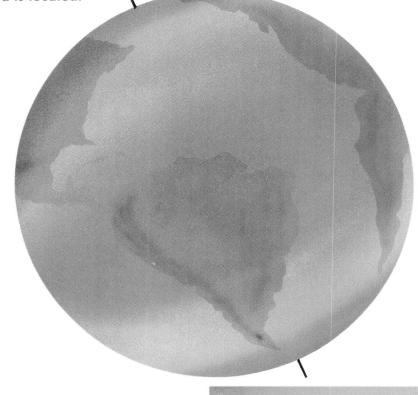

Tropical zones are located along the equator where the temperatures are high.

The angle of the sun is low in the polar zones so the temperatures are low all year.

How Bright Is Snow?

Health  Link

Snow can reflect more than 90 percent of the solar radiation it receives. If you've looked at snow on a sunny day, its glare may have hurt your eyes. The reflected light can be so strong that it can cause snow blindness. Do some research on snow blindness. Learn what it does to the eyes and how to protect yourself from it. Make a poster or give an oral report to your classmates on protecting the eyes from snow blindness.

Inuit people wear goggles to prevent snow blindness.

streets, absorb more energy than light-colored surfaces, which reflect energy. Soil and rocks absorb energy faster than water, but they also release it faster. More energy is absorbed on a given surface at the times of day when the sun's angle is high. Less energy is absorbed when the sun's angle is low.

The tilt of surfaces on the ground can also change the amount of radiation they receive from the sun. What has different angles on Earth's surface? How might this be heated differently by the sun if it had a different angle or tilt?

If you live in the Northern Hemisphere, the month of June may have little or no snow because this area receives the steepest sun rays and the most hours of sunshine in June. Yet you may have noticed that lakes and oceans are usually warmer in July, August, or September than in June. Some people even wait until July or August before they go swimming in lakes. They know water warms very slowly. Water also cools slowly, but the land cools quickly. How does the temperature of land or water affect the air temperature? To investigate this question, do the following activity.

As you can see from this time-lapse photograph, the sun can still be seen at midnight during the summer in the arctic regions. The sun is lowest in the sky at midnight, yet it doesn't set. Shortly thereafter, the sun begins to rise.

Activity!

Test the Air

Imagine you're at the beach or along the shore of a large lake on a warm summer afternoon. Which is warmer, the air over the land or the air over the water? Why do you think so? Test your hypothesis.

What You Need

2 containers, soil, water, 4 thermometers, masking tape, *Activity Log* page 11

Fill one container half full of soil. Fill the other container half full of water. Tape 1 thermometer against the side of the container so its bulb is 1 cm under the surface of the soil or water. Tape the other thermometer against the side of the container and place so the bulb is 1 cm above the surface. Place the boxes side by side in direct sunlight. Read and record the temperature of each thermometer every min for 10 mins. Make a graph in your *Activity Log* comparing the time in mins against the temperature for both soil and water and the air above each. In which container did the temperature rise faster? How did the soil or water temperature affect the temperature of the air above? Do your data support your hypothesis about the temperature of air over land and over water? Explain your results in your *Activity Log.* How do large bodies of water and large areas of dark-colored soil affect air temperatures around the globe?

Air Pressure and Wind

You've experimented to see how surface temperatures can affect air temperatures. Now begin to think of the atmosphere as many air masses, each with its own temperature. **Air masses** are large bodies of air with similar temperatures and amounts of moisture. Temperature differences also create differences in air pressure. **Pressure** is force acting over an area. Just as air in a balloon has pressure and pushes against the sides of

the balloon, air in Earth's atmosphere has pressure and pushes against Earth and objects on it.

Overall, our atmosphere has a mass of about 5 billion tons.

Air pressure is greatest at sea level.

At a height of 5.5 kilometers, air pressure decreases 50 percent from sea level value. Air pressure decreases 25 percent from sea level value at a height of 2.5 kilometers.

34

As the plane rises higher into the atmosphere, the air molecules around it are further apart.

As the plane rises above the ground, there is less and less air above it. Therefore, the amount of air above the plane has less mass. Thus, the air exerts less pressure.

If you were to lie down at the beach and let your friends cover you with sand, you'd feel mass pressing on you. The more sand your friends piled on you, the more mass and pressure you'd feel. Air pressure is similar. The more air there is above you, the more mass it has and the greater its pressure against you.

Study the picture above showing the spacing among air molecules higher in the atmosphere. Notice the number of air molecules above the plane as it rises. Most of the time you don't feel air pressure, but if the pressure changes suddenly, you may feel its effects. Have you ever ridden in a car in the mountains, flown in an airplane, or gone to the top of a tall building in a fast elevator? If you have, you may have felt your ears plug up, or you may have even felt them "pop." What causes this feeling?

Why do we care about air pressure? Well, difference in air pressure is a major factor in causing masses of air to move.

The motion of air is vital in keeping the temperature of Earth just right for life. If the air moved only up and down, the tropics would become too hot for humans to bear. In the polar zones, cold air would settle and the areas would become exceedingly cold. In the temperate zones, weather and temperatures would change from season to season, but they'd change very little from day to day. Fortunately, air does move across Earth's surface, making temperatures all over the world more moderate and varied. To see how air pressure can make an air mass move, do the Try This Activity on the next page.

Activity!

Interaction in a Two-Balloon System

What You Need

2 large round balloons, small thread spool, Activity Log page 12

Work with a partner. Blow up one balloon half way. Twist the neck and then stretch it over one end of the small spool. Keep the balloon twisted so the air doesn't escape. Now blow up the second balloon until it is nearly full. Twist the neck of the second balloon and stretch it over the free end of the spool. Keep both balloons twisted so no air can escape. Before you go on, predict: If you hold the spool and let the balloons untwist, what will happen? Now try it. What happened? In your *Activity Log*, draw the balloons and spool before you untwisted them and after you let their twisted ends unwind. Describe the interaction you observed in this system and explain.

As the activity you just did showed, a change in air pressure can move air. The movement of air from areas of high pressure to areas of low pressure is called **wind.** The greater the difference in air pressure, the faster the wind. If the difference is slight, you may feel a gentle breeze. If the difference is great, air may rush to the low-pressure area at speeds that can flatten buildings. See how much wind speeds can vary in the chart below.

You can observe how objects are affected by the wind. The Beaufort Wind Scale can help determine wind speeds.

	Type of Wind	km/h	m/h	Observations
0	Calm	< 1	< 1	Calm; smoke rises straight up
1	Light Air	1-5	13-18	Weather vanes don't move
2	Light breeze	6-11	4-7	Weather vanes move slightly
3	Gentle breeze	12-19	8-12	Leaves move; flags stretch out
4	Moderate breeze	20-28	13-18	Small branches sway
5	Fresh breeze	29-38	19-24	Trees sway; whitecaps on ponds
6	Strong breeze	39-49	25-31	Large branches sway
7	Moderate gale	50-61	32-38	Hard to walk into the wind
8	Fresh gale	62-74	39-46	Branches break off trees
9	Strong gale	75-88	47-54	Shingles blow off roofs
10	Whole gale	89-102	55-63	Trees are uprooted
11	Storm	103-117	64-73	Extensive damage
12	Hurricane	118 +	74 +	Violent destruction

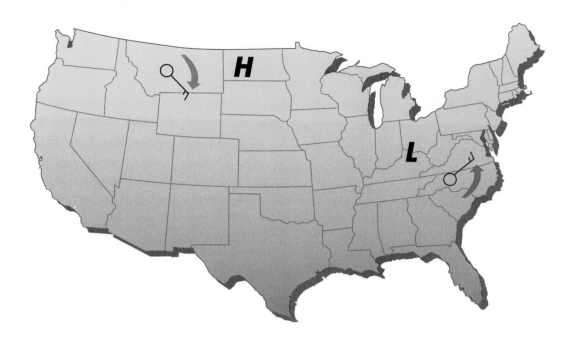

Minds On! Study the weather map. The wind direction at each station is indicated by flag symbols. Think of the flags as arrows with feathers. Note the areas of high and low pressure. What is the general flow of air around each? When you observe the weather each day, use the Beaufort Wind Scale. Include these observations in your weather-watch data. ●

How do you think air temperature is affected by wind? Have you ever heard of the wind-chill factor? What do you think it is? What's the relationship between air temperature, strong winds, and the wind-chill factor?

The arrows fly with the wind. Thus, an arrow shown flying from north to south represents a north wind. The more feathers there are on the arrow, the stronger the wind.

Temperature, Pressure, and Wind

As air warms, its molecules move faster and it expands—that is, its molecules move farther apart. You can picture this if you think about people on a dance floor. If everyone stands still and close together, you can jam a huge crowd of people into the room. If everyone starts to dance slowly, they'll need to move apart a little. The faster they dance, the more room they need, and the farther apart they move.

The dancers are like molecules of air. When air expands, its molecules take up more space without increasing in number. Cool air is more dense than warm air, meaning it has more molecules in a given amount of space. Thus, a cubic meter of warm air has less mass than a cubic meter of cool air. Therefore, a change in air temperature affects air pressure as well. When the air pressure changes due to a change in the temperature, a wind may spring up.

What's the Temperature?

Locate the following pairs of cities on a map. Notice that they're about equally far from the equator. Do library research to compare their average daytime temperatures in winter and summer. But before you research, predict the temperatures and give reasons for your predictions. During the summer, which city would you expect to have higher daytime temperatures—San Francisco or Sacramento, California? Orlando or Cocoa Beach, Florida? Port Gentil, Gabon, or Nairobi, Kenya? Beirut, Lebanon, or Baghdad, Iraq? Does your research support your predictions?

Another example of air pressure at work occurs every time you inhale. When you inhale, you create low pressure in your lungs. That's how you breathe. Your muscles work to expand the space, the air molecules already in your lungs move apart, and the pressure drops. Since the

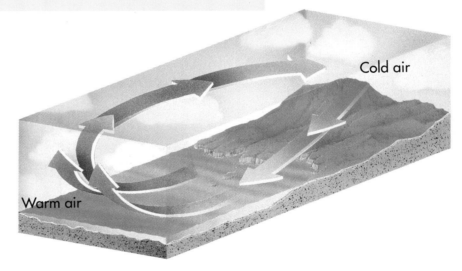

Land Breeze
*The air is warmer at night over the ocean, and warm air is less dense than cool air. Therefore, cooler air from the land rushes over the ocean to replace the warm air in a **land breeze**.*

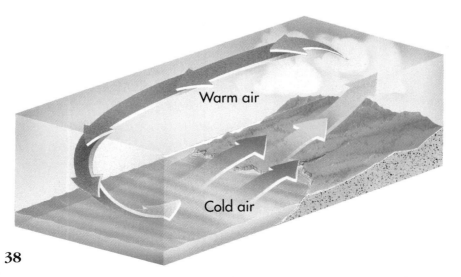

Sea Breeze
*During the day, the air is warmer over the land. Since warm air is less dense than cool air, the warm air rises. Cooler air rushes from over the ocean to the land in a **sea breeze**.*

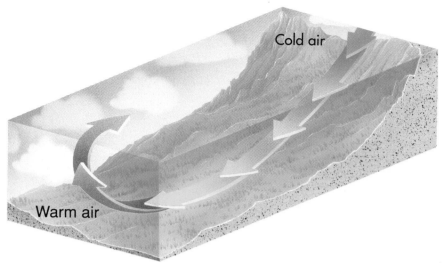

Cold air

Warm air

Mountain Breeze
*At night, the mountainsides and the air above them cool faster than the valley floor. The cooler, dense air flows down the mountainsides as a **mountain breeze**.*

air pressure outside your body is now higher than the air pressure inside your lungs, air rushes in to fill your lungs. Now can you explain how your body changes air pressure so that you can exhale?

You know that differences in pressure create winds. Did you know that most objects in the path of

wind can change the wind's direction or its velocity, unless the wind is very strong? Wind swirls around trees and buildings. When channeled into a narrow corridor between buildings or rocks, wind speeds can change dramatically.

Just as winds flow in patterns around buildings,

certain predictable global wind patterns exist worldwide. Differences in temperature produce patterns of pressure systems called highs and lows all over Earth's surface. The diagram on the following page shows the major wind belts on the planet.

Valley Breeze
*As the warm air over the mountain rises, the cooler air from the valley floor, called a **valley breeze**, moves up the sides of the mountain. Winds from the valley rise up the mountainsides during the day.*

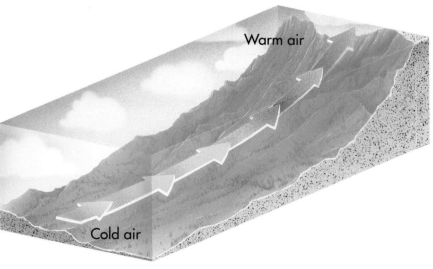

Warm air

Cold air

There is very little wind in the doldrums. History is full of accounts of sailors whose ships have been stranded in the doldrums. The winds died, the sea turned as smooth as glass, and the sailors spent days in the scorching heat, waiting for a breeze to fill their sails.

By contrast, the wind belts north and south of the dol-drums produce steady, dependable winds that were good luck to the sailing ships of old. These wind belts were so important to sailors who traded overseas that they were named the trade winds. However, the trade winds do not move directly north or south.

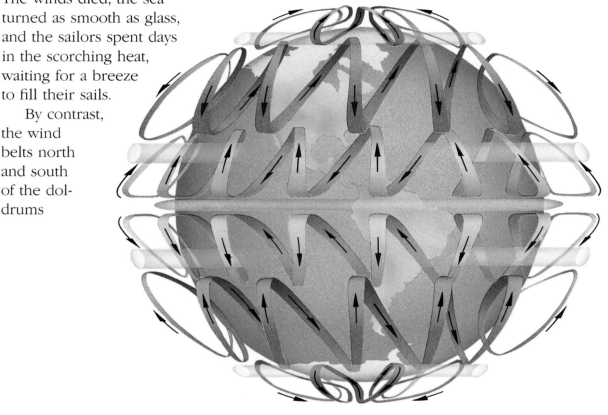

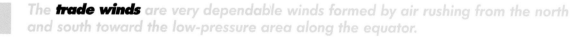

The **trade winds** are very dependable winds formed by air rushing from the north and south toward the low-pressure area along the equator.

Turned by Earth's rotation, the **prevailing westerlies** move from southwest to north-east in the Northern Hemisphere and from northwest to southeast in the Southern Hemisphere.

Hot air along the equator rises, creating an area of low pressure called the **dol-drums** (dōl´ drəmz).

In the polar regions, cold dense air flowing towards the equator creates winds. These winds, too, are turned by Earth's rotation, and are called the **polar easter-lies.**

Professor Coriolis discovered that winds turn from their straight path as they move over the rotating surface of Earth.

The movement of Earth on its axis causes the trade winds to turn. In the Northern Hemisphere, the trade winds move from northeast to southwest. In the Southern Hemisphere, the trade winds move from southeast to northwest. The tendency of Earth's rotation to turn the winds is called the **Coriolis** (Cor´ē ō´ lez) **effect.** This force is named after Professor Gaspard Gustave de Coriolis, who, in 1835, studied how smaller objects move over the surface of larger rotating objects and are sent off their straight path. The

larger rotating object in this case is Earth, with the wind sent off its path due to Earth's rotation.

Meanwhile, what is happening to the warm air that was pushed up at the equator? The rising air expands and gets cooler due to its expansion. Once the air is high in the atmosphere, it begins to move north or south, away from the equator. At this height, it cools, becomes dense, and sinks near 30 degrees latitude. Because the air moves straight down, there is little wind in the horse latitudes, as these belts are called. According to legend, they were named centuries ago

by sailors who came to a halt in these windless regions and had to conserve water. The horses they were transporting as cargo had to be thrown overboard because of the low water supply.

The cool descending air at the horse latitudes causes an area of high pressure. Air rushes south from this high-pressure area and helps create the trade winds. The air flowing north from the horse latitudes produces the prevailing westerlies (prə vā´ ling wes´ tər lēs).(Note that winds are named according to the direction from which they blow.)

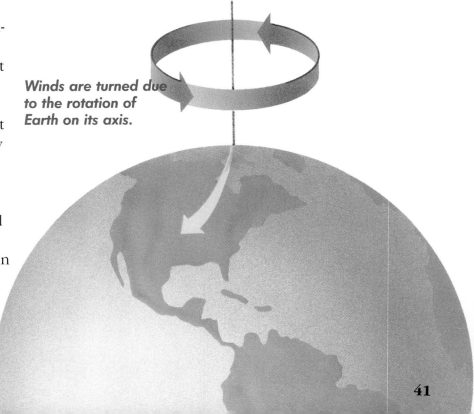

Winds are turned due to the rotation of Earth on its axis.

*The strongest and fastest global winds, called **jet streams,** can cause lines of clouds to form.*

Jet streams rush over the temperate zones like giant rivers near the top of the troposphere. Their speeds range from 120–560 kilometers (75–350 miles) per hour. If the jet streams were near Earth's surface, such wind speeds would destroy much of what lay in their paths. These winds were discovered by pilots during World War II. Sometimes their planes could not move forward against them—even at full power. Pilots today avoid these winds when they're flying in the opposite direction. However, when they're flying from west to east, they often hitch a ride on the jet stream to shorten their flight time and save fuel.

These pressure systems and prevailing winds influence weather all over the world. The winds influence the direction in which weather systems move. In which direction do you think weather systems move in the temperate zones?

Winds flowing from an area of high pressure to an area of low pressure usually don't move in a straight line because of the rotation of Earth. Rather, the winds tend to spiral around low- and high-pressure centers.

*In the northern hemisphere, winds move counterclockwise around **low-pressure centers** that contain rising warm air.*

Warm air

Descriptive Poetry

Read the stanza below from *The Rime of the Ancient Mariner*, by Samuel Taylor Coleridge. In what part of the ocean might "we" be? Suggest two possibilities.

Day after day, day after day,
We stuck, nor breath nor motion;
As idle as a painted ship
Upon a painted ocean.

In the northern hemisphere, winds move clockwise around **high-pressure centers** that contain sinking cold air.

Cold air

In the southern hemisphere, winds move clockwise around low-pressure centers and counterclockwise around high-pressure centers.

Feeling the Pressure

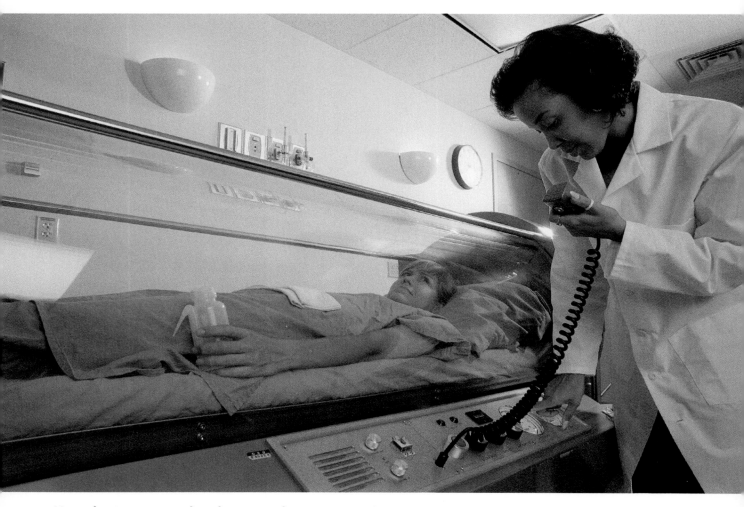

Hyperbaric oxygen chambers supply patients with air consisting of 100 percent oxygen at three times the pressure of the atmosphere.

In order to better understand our atmosphere and how pressure changes, we use barometers to measure the actual amount of pressure. **Barometers** allow scientists to watch daily pressure changes and determine how the changes may affect the temperature and weather of an area. You can measure the changes in air pressure with a barometer.

Scientists study the atmospheric pressure for many reasons; the main reasons may be to predict the weather and to understand global climates. Knowledge of the atmosphere has even also allowed people to become healthier and have better medical treatment due to a new kind of therapy.

Hyperbaric Oxygen Chambers

Differences in air pressure can influence the amount of oxygen people receive while breathing. People usually breathe air containing 21 percent oxygen. But, some medical patients need more oxygen in their blood. A hyperbaric (hī pər bâr′ ik) oxygen chamber allows more oxygen to enter the blood.

Have you ever dived several feet below the surface in a lake, ocean, or pool? A patient in a hyperbaric oxygen chamber feels pressure like that on her or his skin. From outside the airtight chamber, a trained respiratory therapist monitors the patient for a treatment 90 to 120 minutes long.

Hyperbaric therapy increases the oxygen content of the blood and makes blood vessels smaller in diameter. It also helps to form new blood vessels that carry blood to damaged tissues, and it discourages the growth of microorganisms that lead to infections. Some patients treated by hyperbaric therapy include babies born before their lungs have developed, people with burns or infections, and victims of smoke inhalation or carbon-monoxide poisoning.

Sum It Up

The temperature and pressure of the atmosphere are always changing. Measuring and tracking them give us a better understanding of how the atmosphere affects us. The temperature and pressure of the atmosphere interact with one another and have a daily influence on you, whether you live at the top of a mountain, near the sea, or far inland. If you have a better understanding of Earth's atmosphere and how its properties affect wind and global temperature differences, you'll be able to determine what tomorrow's temperature might be or even how the overall climate of an area might change years from now.

Critical Thinking

1. How could you use your shadow to tell the time on a sunny day?

2. Which beach would be cooler to the touch on a sunny day—a Jamaican beach made of shells and coral or a beach in Hawaii made of black sand?

3. Suppose you noticed your bike tire was a little flat when you began your ride on the blacktopped street to your friend's house. When you arrived 15 minutes later, the tire wasn't flat at all. Explain.

4. A drinking straw works because of air pressure. Explain how differences in air pressure cause a liquid to flow through the straw and into your mouth.

5. Suppose it's a very cold day and you'll be outside for an hour or so. The sun is shining. Should you wear dark blue or yellow to stay warmer? Explain.

Why Does It Rain and Snow?

As the rains of spring fall and the snows of winter blow, Earth receives water. Will the skies ever run out of water to replenish Earth?

In some parts of the world, dry, thirsty land needs rain. For lack of rain crops wither and die, and many people starve. In recent years, millions of

Flood waters can cause great destruction.

people in Ethiopia have starved, partly due to many years of drought. Yet in Bangladesh, Jamaica, the southeastern United States, and elsewhere, people have lost their lives and homes in floods caused by heavy rains. In a single day in 1952, more than 183 centimeters (about 73 inches) of rain fell on La Reunion, an island in the Indian Ocean. Death Valley, California, has received only a little more rain than that in 40 years! What creates the rain on which all life depends? What determines where it falls?

Part of the solution to the mystery of rain lies in what you've learned about the system we call the atmosphere. What do you know about interactions in the atmosphere that produce temperature differences, air pressure, and wind?

Minds On! Think about how rain or snow affects your life. In what ways do you depend upon rain or snow? What happens when your community receives too much? What happens where there isn't enough? Write your answers in your *Activity Log* page 13.

Within the atmosphere clouds form, and rain and snow may fall to Earth. What factors influence the formation of clouds?

47

Activity!

How Do Rivers, Lakes, and Oceans Help To Form Clouds?

Water is found in all forms on Earth's surface. You see water in puddles, rivers, lakes, and oceans. But have you ever seen water in the air? Do this activity to observe the characteristics of water vapor.

What You Need

hot tap water
2 identical containers
3 ice cubes
refrigerator or freezer
food coloring
Activity Log pages 14–15

What To Do

1 Chill 1 container. You may put it in a refrigerator or on ice for about 10 minutes.

2 When the container is very cold, slowly and carefully add very hot tap water to the

other container until it is half full, and add 2 drops of food coloring to the warm water. *Safety Tip:* Be careful when handling the hot water. Do not burn yourself.

3 Place the cold container upside-down on top of the container with warm water, fitting the mouths together carefully.

Safety!

See the *Safety Tip* in step 2.

4 Place the ice cubes on top of the chilled container. What do you think will happen? Write your prediction in your *Activity Log.*

5 Take turns observing the container for about 30 mins. Record your observations in your *Activity Log.*

What Happened?

1. What did you observe just after you put the chilled container over the container of hot water?
2. Where did this take place? Why?
3. What happened on the top and sides of the upper container? Where did the water come from?

What Now?

1. Suppose you were to leave the two containers in place for a few days. What would eventually happen to the water that appeared in the upper container?
2. How could this process help you explain how clouds form? Where would you expect to find more clouds—over the ocean or over a desert? Why?
3. Think about what happened as the water vapor rose and cooled. How does this help explain how oceans and lakes stay full even though they release water vapor into the air?

EXPLORE

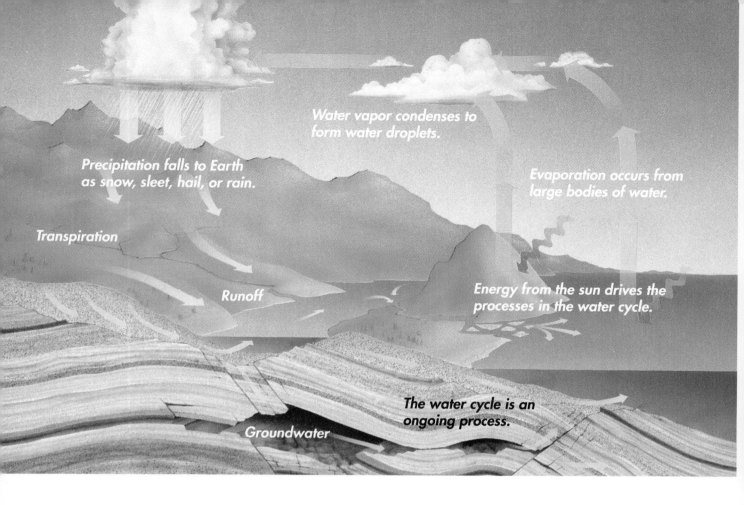

Water vapor condenses to form water droplets.

Precipitation falls to Earth as snow, sleet, hail, or rain.

Evaporation occurs from large bodies of water.

Transpiration

Runoff

Energy from the sun drives the processes in the water cycle.

The water cycle is an ongoing process.

Groundwater

Water Comes and Goes

What you observed happening in the container in the Explore Activity is a model of the **water cycle.** Through the process of **evaporation**, liquid water changes to water vapor, an invisible gas. In the Explore Activity, the water vapor increased the humidity in the upper bottle when it entered the air. **Humidity** is a measure of the amount of water vapor in the air. In your experiment, the warm, moist air in the lower container rose and met the cooler air in the upper container. This process occurs in the atmosphere over bodies of water. Why do places near large bodies of water, like Miami, Florida or Portland, Oregon, have more water vapor in the air than desert areas like Las Vegas, Nevada?

As the water vapor cooled in the upper container, it formed tiny water droplets through a process called **condensation** (kon den sā´ shən), water changing state from gas to liquid. In clouds, the droplets condense around tiny particles that are always present in the atmosphere. These particles include dust, smoke, salt crystals, and soil. Scientists call these cloud particles condensation nuclei (nü´ klē ī).

When the water droplets condensed on the cold sides of the container in the Explore Activity on page 48–49, they combined into larger drops. As they became more massive, they fell down the sides of the jar. When water droplets combine to form larger drops and become massive enough to fall in the atmosphere, the process is called **precipitation.** When water vapor condenses on something cold on the ground, these water droplets are called **dew.** What time of day is dew likely to form? Why?

In Lesson 1, you discovered that as air rises, it cools. To understand why water vapor condenses, or turns into water, as the air cools, you must understand relative humidity. Do the Try This Activity to discover what relative humidity is.

Humidity is always high in jungles, such as this one in Costa Rica.

TRY THIS
Activity!

See Relative Amounts of Humidity

What does *relative humidity* mean? To what is it relative?

What You Need
3 sizes of plastic glasses (small, medium, large) graduated cylinder water
Activity Log **page 16**

Use the graduated cylinder to find the volume or capacity of each glass. Make a drawing of each glass and record the volume of each glass in your *Activity Log.*

Fill the small glass with water. What percent of its volume or holding capacity is filled? Pour the water from the small glass into the medium-sized one. What happened to the actual amount or volume of water? What percent of the medium-sized glass is filled with water? Now repeat the process with the large glass. What percent of the large glass is filled with water?

Water vapor can condense onto flowers.

You've just determined the relationship between the amount of water in a glass and the amount of water the glass could hold if it had been full. The weather service does a similar analysis to determine relative humidity.

A percentage, called **relative humidity,** is used to compare the amount of water vapor in the air to the amount of water vapor it could hold at its present temperature. If the relative humidity is 25 percent, the air contains 25 percent or one-fourth of the amount of water vapor it could hold at its present temperature. If the relative humidity is 100 percent, the air has all the water vapor it can hold at that temperature.

As air cools, its relative humidity increases. As air warms, its relative humidity decreases.

In the activity, the glasses represented the capacity, or volume, of water that air could hold if it were full. The water represented the actual amount of water vapor in the air. The larger glass represented warmer air and the small glass represented cooler air.

Humidity, or the amount of moisture in the air, shouldn't be confused with relative humidity. It may be very humid on a hot summer day, but the relative humidity would be low. You discovered that warm air could hold more water vapor than cold air, but if the air was warmed and the amount of water vapor didn't change, its relative humidity decreased because the warm air took up more space. Likewise, when air cools and the amount of water does not change, the relative-humidity increases. It's just like pouring a glass of water into another glass half its size, so that the small glass is 100 percent full.

As air cools, its relative humidity increases. As air warms, its relative humidity

decreases. At what time of day is the relative humidity greatest? At what time of day is the air usually driest?

Minds On! Suppose that you made a sandwich for your school lunch every evening. You probably put the sandwich in a plastic bag and seal it and place it in the refrigerator. Let's say that one day you got up later than usual and missed breakfast. On the way to school you decided to eat the sandwich. When you took the sandwich out of the sealed plastic bag, you found it was wet and soggy. Write what you think happened in your *Activity Log* page 17. ●

Both the temperature and the amount of water vapor in the air affect daily weather changes. Without water vapor, there would be no precipitation.

The amount of water vapor in the air depends partly upon the amount of water available. Most water vapor evaporates into the air from bodies of water or from plants. Thus, places near oceans, lakes, and forests usually have more water vapor in the air than do places without bodies of water or vegetation.

The temperature affects

the amount of water vapor in the air as well. Land and bodies of water warm the air above them. As the air warms, it rises, carrying the water vapor with it. As the air rises higher into the atmosphere, it cools. As it cools, its relative humidity increases. When the relative humidity reaches 100 percent, the air contains all of the water vapor it can hold at that temperature. .If the air becomes cooler, water vapor begins to condense, forming liquid water droplets. The temperature at which condensation occurs is called the **dew point.** To investigate this concept, do the Try This Activity.

Dew forms on objects when the temperature of the air reaches the dew point. Dew can also freeze and become frost.

Activity!

Where Is Your Room's Dew Point?

You can bring the air in your classroom to its dew point.

What You Need

shiny tin or aluminum can, thermometer, stirring rod, ice, water, *Activity Log* page 18

Fill the can half full of room-temperature water. Use the thermometer to measure the temperature of the water. Slowly add pieces of ice to the water and stir slowly and carefully with the stirring rod. Have an alert partner observe the outsides of the can for evidence of condensation. The instant you see the shiny surface become dull or cloudy, read the thermometer and record the temperature. What was the temperature of the water when the moisture film on the can first appeared? Compare your temperature with that obtained by other groups. Where did the water film on the can come from? In your *Activity Log,* describe what happened to the air near the can to produce the water film.

Types of Clouds

Clouds are often associated with weather patterns. They can indicate the stability of the atmosphere. Different atmospheric conditions form different types of clouds.

Cumulus (kū´ myə ləs) clouds are found in globular masses and resemble pieces of cauliflower. They often extend very high in the sky and are associated with fair weather.

Cirrus (sûr əs) clouds are wispy clouds that form high in the sky. Some types of cirrus clouds are called "mare's tails" to describe their appearance. Since they form high in the atmosphere where the temperature is very low, these clouds contain tiny crystals of ice. Cirrus clouds may appear shortly before a change in the weather.

Nimbus (nim´ bəs) cloud is the name given to a rain-bearing cloud. A nimbus cloud appears dark and thick or dense. The term nimbus can also be added to the names of other clouds. For example, rain-bearing cumulus clouds are dark instead of white at the bottom, and are called cumulonimbus clouds.

Stratus (stra təs) clouds form relatively near Earth's surface in flat layers like a blanket. They're often connected with stormy weather.

In the poem, "I Wandered Lonely as a Cloud," by William Wordsworth, the poet's comparison works for some clouds, but not all clouds are lonely. Some gather in banks or layers. Others tower to several kilometers thick. Air currents in the cloud keep the water droplets in motion. These droplets of water collide, or bump into each other. Water droplets usually join and form larger drops. When the drops have reached a certain size, they may eventually fall to Earth. If they reach the surface as liquid water, the precipitation is called rain.

If raindrops pass through air that has a temperature below freezing, the raindrops may freeze and become sleet. Sometimes winds toss the frozen drops around through warm and cold layers of air. Many layers of ice build up, and the precipitation falls to Earth as hail. Hailstones can be as big as baseballs and can cause damage.

Sometimes the air is so cold that water vapor condenses into tiny ice crystals instead of tiny water droplets. As you've read, cirrus clouds are made of ice crystals and tiny water droplets. Often ice crystals collect and form a snowflake. When snowflakes fall, we call the precipitation snow.

Fog is a stratus cloud that forms on or close to the ground. Fog often forms over large bodies of water.

Hail can cause considerable damage to objects such as airplanes.

Hailstones vary in size, but some can become quite large.

Rainbows, Mirages, and Sundogs

"Made of tiny ice crystals, they form about 16 miles above the ground, which makes them twice as high as the highest ordinary clouds...

Mother-of-pearl clouds are especially beautiful when seen a bit to the left or right of the setting Sun. Sometimes they are seen in broad banks, shining with the brilliance and rich colors of fish scales. An entire cloud bank may appear almost a single color, while the edges may glisten with all the colors of the rainbow."

In his handbook, *Rainbows, Mirages, and Sundogs,* Roy Gallant gives the description above of mother-of-pearl clouds. Have you ever seen them? List as many color words and phrases as you can that might describe these clouds. You might think of words like *shiny* or *pearly,* but

Mother-of-pearl clouds are often very colorful.

would you have used Gallant's description, *fish scales*? Why is *fish scales* exactly the right phrase for mother-of-pearl clouds? What other things reflect light like fish scales? Write your list of words and phrases in your **Activity Log** page 19. Then write a descriptive paragraph, song, or poem using your list of words and phrases.

Precipitation and temperature are two major factors that determine the climate of a region. What are the average temperature and precipitation rate for your region?

In Lesson 1, you learned about the major climate zones. Within these major zones are smaller climate zones known as meso climates and micro climates. **Meso climates** are the weather conditions of large areas such as mountain ranges or plains. **Micro climates** consist of a single forest, field, or even the area around a single building.

Climate zones are very different, and so are the lifestyles of the people who live in them. Each type of landform has its characteristic climate, and each climate affects the people who live in the area. The climate often determines the way people make their living. For example, you couldn't make a living selling shorts in the polar zones. To grow pineapples, you'd have to live in a moist, tropical climate. The houses humans build, the clothing they wear, and their recreation are all influenced by the climate.

GLOBAL PERSPECTIVE

Seasonal Winds

About half of Earth's people depend upon winds called monsoons for their food supply. **Monsoons** are regional, seasonal winds that affect large parts of the globe. These winds contain water vapor and can bring heavy precipitation. They blow across Southeast Asia, India, Pakistan, China, Japan, Australia, parts of Africa, and the southwestern United States. Some of the most heavily-populated countries in the world lie in monsoon areas.

The largest monsoon is in southern Asia and crosses India and Pakistan. It's caused by seasonal temperature differences among the Indian Ocean, the Arabian Sea, and the land of central Asia.

In winter, the land is colder than the ocean. Therefore, the air pressure over central Asia is higher than the air pressure over the water. Cool, dry air blows to the southwest from Asia to the Indian Ocean, crossing India and all of southern Asia on its way. This wind is called the winter monsoon.

During the summer, the land in Asia is warmer than the Indian Ocean. The moist air over the ocean blows to the northeast, carrying vast quantities of water vapor. In parts of Bangladesh, this summer monsoon can dump as much as 1,107 centimeters (about 440 inches) of rain—more than ten times the average annual rainfall for the United States. Farmers depend on the summer monsoon for rain to water the crops. However, these life-giving rains can also cause death and destruction.

Monsoons bring rain to this community in Zaire.

Modifying the Weather

Minds On! Having more knowledge about winds, temperature, and air pressure allows people to learn more about predicting the weather. Have you ever wondered what would happen if people could change the weather or modify it for a particular need? In your ***Activity Log*** page 20, write some ideas for changing the weather. What would you do to the weather? How would your change benefit you and others? Discuss your ideas with your classmates. ●

To produce precipitation, water drops or ice crystals in the clouds must become big enough to fall to Earth. Researchers use this fact to create or increase precipitation in clouds with the technique of cloud seeding.

To seed clouds, large condensation nuclei such as salt crystals or silver iodide are dropped from airplanes into large, thick clouds. Usually these clouds are already producing some precipitation. Cloud seeding can add 10 to 20 percent.

Language Arts Link

People Changing Climates

Climate can be changed by human activity. In western Europe and Africa, pollution from industrial countries has significantly changed the climate. Discover how this occurs and write a newspaper article on this topic for publication in your school. What responsibility do citizens have for resolving these pollution problems? Try to answer these questions in your article. In a small group, share your articles and debate possible solutions.

Substances that will act as condensation nuclei are dropped into clouds from airplanes.

Weather-Modification Meteorologists

Meteorology is the study of atmospheric and weather conditions. Researchers known as weather-modification meteorologists study weather patterns and their movements. They also are responsible for tracking clouds to use in the cloud-seeding process. When clouds move near the area, meteorologists predict the direction the clouds will go.

When the right kind of cloud is in position, the weather-modification meteorologists send up pilots. Throughout the cloud-seeding process, the meteorologists watch the radar, observing changes in the cloud. They also ask the pilots for specific information that explains more about the cloud. It's up to the meteorologist to decide where the pilots should place the cloud-seeding material and how long the seeding should continue. Weather-modification meteorologists are required to have a Bachelor of Science degree or a Master's Degree in meteorology.

We still have a lot to learn about weather systems and their interactions in order to properly modify the weather. But, with weather-modification meteorologists studying and researching our atmosphere, we may one day be able not only to modify weather systems, but also to better understand and adapt to weather changes.

Meterologists often work with highly technical equipment.

Sum It Up

You're affected by the weather every day. The rain, snow, and temperature determine what you're going to do, wear, and eat. With your knowledge of the atmospheric conditions, you can better understand why the weather or climate is the way it is. Many factors influence the weather and how it interacts with Earth's surface. Weather conditions affect the entire world's climate, food supply, and people.

Critical Thinking

1. How might sleet form?
2. If one cubic meter of air at 25°C can hold 15 grams of water vapor but it's only holding 5 grams, what is its relative humidity?
3. When does dew form?
4. Two rooms have the same amount of water vapor. One room, though, is cooler than the other. Which room has the greater relative humidity? Explain.
5. Describe the appearance of a nimbostratus cloud. What kind of weather would you expect if nimbostratus clouds were overhead?

What Will the Weather Be Tomorrow?

What are you planning to do this weekend? It's more than likely that your plans will be affected in some way by the weather. What will the weather be like this weekend? Up to now, you've relied on a professional weather forecaster. But soon you'll discover for yourself how weather patterns are predicted and what you need to know to be able to predict the weather.

Minds On! Why is it important to be able to predict the weather? Suppose you're a weather forecaster for a television station and you're required to make a weather report for the six o'clock news every day. What information would you include in your reports? Prepare a weather report for today based on information that you already know. Write your weather report in your *Activity Log*, page 21.

On July 11, 1991, about 50,000 people flew to Hawaii to watch an eclipse of the sun. They'd made reservations a year in advance, and they filled every hotel room on the island. Unfortunately, at the moment when the moon moved between the sun and Earth, people at sea level were unable to see the eclipse! Dense clouds blanketed the island, and a fog bank rolled in just as the eclipse began. Could weather forecasters have predicted the cloud cover in time for people to cancel their trips?

How would they have predicted it?

In large and small ways, the weather has always been important to humans. It influences their clothing, their activities, and where they take shelter. Studies have even been conducted to determine if weather affects people's attitudes. More importantly, weather can cause dangerous conditions or even deaths. Therefore, weather predicting has been a major human activity for thousands of years.

By the 13th century B.C., the Chinese were experimenting with weather prediction. They used Anyang oracle bones in 1220 B.C. to help record rainfall, snow, and wind direction. They understood the water cycle as early as the fourth century B.C. By measuring the change in masses of feathers and charcoal, which hold moisture, they measured changes in humidity. How do you think the mass of these objects related to the humidity of the air? By the 13th century A.D., Chinese meteorologists were using gauges to measure rain and snow depth. In the 14th century A.D., kites and anemometers helped them study the upper atmosphere.

Greek scientists also studied weather. Theophratus, a pupil of Aristotle's, wrote *The Book of Signs* more than 2,000 years ago. In it he described 200 signs of coming weather, such as changes in animal behavior. Many of his signs have proved useful in weather forecasting today.

Wherever they lived, when scientists began to predict weather they studied some of the same information you read in the first three lessons of this unit. Of the information you've already studied, what facts do you think would help scientists most? Why?

In this lesson, you'll learn how meteorologists use what they know about atmosphere, temperature, air pressure, and humidity to predict the weather. You'll also learn more about what causes weather to change. First let's figure out how to interpret a professional weather map.

Weather conditions can change rapidly in mountainous regions of Hawaii.

Activity!

Predicting the Weather

Daily weather data are collected at recording stations all over the world. When the data are placed on a weather map, they provide information that forecasters use to predict weather. The information given on weather maps may help you understand what causes weather and why it changes. This activity will give you a chance to interpret weather conditions and to predict changes.

What You Need

Activity Log pages 22–23

What To Do

1 On the weather map, find the location of the weather-station model closest to where you live. Using the map key and the information at that station, describe the weather conditions in your *Activity Log*.

2 Locate the high-pressure system. What is the general sky condition in the area around the high? Now locate the low. What general sky conditions exist in the area of the low?

3 Study the wind arrows at stations around the high and the low. Does air move into or out of a high-pressure system? How does the air move in a low-pressure system?

4 Look at the temperature data for Denver, Colorado. What is the air temperature? What does the number below that represent? How many degrees' difference is there between these two temperatures in Denver? Now check the same data for Louisville, Kentucky. How do they compare? Make a note of the difference between these two temperatures. You'll use that information in the next part of this activity.

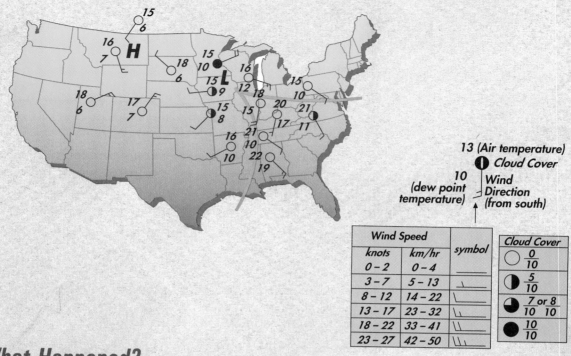

Wind Speed

Wind Speed		symbol
knots	km/hr	
0 – 2	0 – 4	
3 – 7	5 – 13	╱
8 – 12	14 – 22	╲
13 – 17	23 – 32	╲╲
18 – 22	33 – 41	╲╲╲
23 – 27	42 – 50	╲╲╲╲

13 (Air temperature)
Cloud Cover
10 (dew point temperature)
Wind Direction (from south)

Cloud Cover	
○	0/10
◐	5/10
◕	7 or 8 / 10 10
●	10/10

What Happened?

Notice the two dark lines curving away from the low-pressure area. The general weather conditions in the areas next to these lines will help you to understand what these dark lines represent.

1. Find the locations of the three weather stations just west of the dark line extending south of the low. Note their reported air temperatures and dew-point temperatures. Now locate the three stations just east of that same dark line. How do the air temperatures and dew-point temperatures of these stations compare with those on the west side of the line? On which side of the line does the air have more moisture or humidity? (You may wish to look back at Lesson 3 to help you answer this question.)

2. Investigate the air temperatures and dew-point temperatures on either side of the other dark line. Compare the atmospheric conditions on either side of this boundary.

What Now?

You can assume that the cold air mass will move from west to east. The warm air mass will move more slowly to the north. Use this information and data from the map to make some weather predictions.

1. Will it be warmer or cooler in Nashville, Tennessee, tomorrow? Why do you think so?

2. As the low-pressure system moves eastward, how will the sky conditions change in the Minneapolis area?

EXPLORE

What Makes Up Weather?

In the weather-map Explore Activity on pages 62–63, you examined the temperature and the amount of moisture of several masses of air. Meteorologists use weather maps just as you did in the activity. Meteorologists observe air masses carefully and track their movement. They know that air masses, their movement, and the way they interact with each other determine weather conditions.

The place where an air mass forms is called its **source area.** When an air mass moves to another place, it carries its temperature and humidity with it. Meteorologists predicting weather changes can rely on this fact.

As an air mass moves, it comes in contact with other air masses with different temperatures and amounts of moisture. The air masses interact with one another at their boundaries and produce changes that can often be predicted. The boundary between the air masses, where the interaction takes place, is called a **front.** As the air masses move, the front moves with them.

Air masses seldom move at the same speed. The mass that is moving faster determines the way the two masses will interact, because the faster-moving mass overcomes the slower one. Most stormlike weather conditions take place along fronts.

A **cold front** forms when a cold air mass moves into a region occupied by a warm air mass. Warm air and cold air don't mix easily. You've discovered that when warm air is forced to rise, it cools and its relative humidity increases. Thus, the water vapor in the air condenses, and forms a line of clouds.

As you can see from the diagram, when a warm mass overtakes a cold air mass that's moving away, a **warm front** develops. The warm air is forced up, and the cooler air remains under the warm, rising air. As the warm air is forced upward, it cools, clouds form, and frequently precipitation develops.

Cold Front
In a cold front denser cold air tends to move under the warm air, forcing it upward along the front.

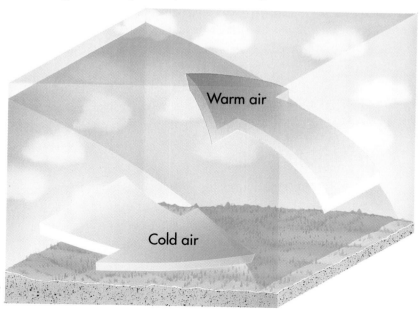

Warm air

Cold air

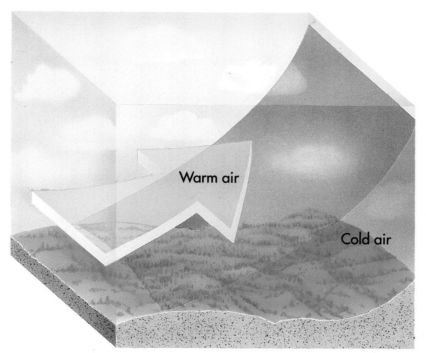

Warm air

Cold air

Warm Front
In a warm front as the warm air advances, it moves up and over the edge of the cold air mass.

Other Types of Fronts

A warm or cold front can stall, or stop moving. Such a front does not advance and is called a **stationary front.**

Another type of front is formed when two cold air masses merge and force the warmer air between them to rise. This is an **occluded** (ə klüd´ əd) **front.**

Fronts cause disturbances in the atmosphere, and therefore, they change the weather. Certain types of weather changes are associated with each type of front. Usually, cold fronts move faster than warm fronts. They also cause air to rise more quickly and at a steeper angle than air along warm fronts. The rapidly-rising air results in the formation of cumulus and cumulonimbus clouds that develop vertically, sometimes reaching great heights. Cold fronts and their clouds may bring heavy precipitation with large drops. However, because cold fronts move fast, the precipitation and other weather conditions they bring are often brief. The front often passes quickly and the skies clear. As the front passes and the cold

Occluded Front
Sometimes the cold air forces the warm air to rise very quickly. If the differences in temperature are slight, the cooler air may rise above the warm air and an occluded front develops.

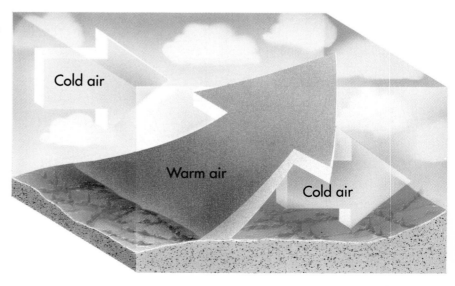

Cold air

Warm air

Cold air

air mass replaces the warmer one, the temperature drops. Now that you know more about fronts, do the Try This Activity.

You may have observed from the Try This Activity that warm fronts usually move more slowly than cold fronts do. The weather changes that warm fronts bring also affect larger areas. The boundary of a warm front isn't as steep as that of a cold front. Thus, the air rises more slowly and is forced aloft, spreading out over a wider area. Usually this results in the formation of thick, layered stratus clouds. Because warm fronts are wide and move slowly, they generally bring steady, long-lasting rain or snow.

With any front, the amount of precipitation depends on how much water vapor is present in the warm air being forced aloft. If the air contains a lot of moisture, the front produces heavy clouds and precipitation as the air cools. If the air being forced aloft is dry, clouds may form but precipitation doesn't develop.

This land in Italy receives little rain, as shown by the cracked surface.

TRY THIS

Activity!

Can You Predict the Weather?

What You Need
**weather maps from your local newspaper
weather watch data
Activity Log page 24**

Study the daily weather-watch data you've been gathering during this unit. Were there any noticeable temperature changes? What may have caused the change? Is there a relationship between sky condition (wind, clouds) and air pressure? Compare this data with the daily weather maps from your local paper. Did a front pass through your area? What data do you have that support this? How much precipitation did your area receive? Record this information in your *Activity Log* page 24.

Math Link

How Fast Do Fronts Move?

Obtain two weather maps for consecutive days from a newspaper. Examine them, paying attention to warm and cold fronts and how their positions have changed. Design a scale to calculate the speed of the moving front. (Hint: To design a scale, find the width of the continental United States in kilometers. Then measure that width on your weather maps. To figure out how many kilometers are equal to 1 cm on your weather map, convert the real-world distance to centimeters and divide that number by the map distance). Assume the two maps were assembled 24 hours apart. Pick one spot on the front and calculate how far it moved in 24 hours. Then calculate how far it traveled in one hour. Try to predict where the weather front may be in 24 hours if it moves at its present speed.

Sometimes weather fronts don't move as expected. A stationary high-pressure system can keep low-pressure systems from moving. When this happens, the area can be deprived of rain, and a crippling drought may even occur. For example, California suffered many dry years in the 1980s and early 1990s. Cold air masses developed over the Pacific Ocean, creating areas of high pressure. For several years in a row, high-pressure systems remained in place during California's rainy season, causing approaching rainstorms to veer around California.

Just the same kind of stationary high-pressure system has often caused disastrous droughts across the world. In Ethiopia, for example, crops fail to grow because of stalled weather patterns.

Predicting Weather

Because weather affects us so strongly, it's helpful to try to predict it. How do meteorologists predict the weather? Each morning, information is gathered by the National Weather Advisory Board. Weather balloons rise more than 32 kilometers (about 20 miles) into the atmosphere, and then burst. The instrument then parachutes back to Earth. Similar weather balloons are launched each day from 700 locations around the world.

At sea, automated buoys gather similar information and relay it back to weather stations by radio. Automated observatories also gather information from mountain tops. Gathering weather information is a cooperative effort. Across the United States, more than 12,000 volunteer observers phone in their information. These people live in rural areas and gather information with thermometers and wind vanes. About 300 observers are located on merchant ships at sea, and almost 4,000 commercial airplane crews report their observations.

Weather balloons carry instruments that transmit information on temperature, wind speed, pressure, and humidity in the upper atmosphere.

Hundreds of weather offices report their information to the National Meteorological Service daily. There, giant computers organize information and create models of the conditions in Earth's atmosphere. The computers also create and print out national and regional weather maps. As you know, weather maps contain information about weather conditions such as wind speed, temperature, and cloud cover. They also show the location of air masses and fronts. These maps are updated every three hours. By comparing two maps made three hours apart, meteorologists can see the direction weather systems are moving and the speed at which they're moving. This helps them predict where those weather systems will go next. You accomplished similar results when you calculated the speed of moving fronts and predicted where they would be in 24 hours in the Math Link on page 67.

Forecasters need information from all over the United States to make a local forecast for 24 hours. To forecast weather for three days, they need information from Europe, Canada, and South America. For a five-day forecast, they need global information. Conditions driving the weather can change quickly, though. If you read a three-day weather forecast on Thursday, you can plan a picnic for Saturday. However, you should check the forecast again on Saturday before leaving the house.

Global weather influences local weather. Thus, weather forecasters need the complete global picture. Each afternoon, the National Meteorological Center issues a 10-day global forecast. The World Meteorological Center, an agency of the United Nations, coordinates watch services worldwide. The cooperative efforts of all those involved from around the world make it possible to piece together a global weather forecast.

Automated sea buoys help to track weather conditions across the oceans.

Weather Predictions of the Past and the Future

Long before meteorologists had developed technological equipment or much scientific knowledge, weather prophets were predicting the weather. They watched weather patterns over the years and learned to connect certain observations with different types of weather. The result has been a number of weather proverbs, or wise sayings. Read the following weather saying and explain why this might be true at times.

"When bats and birds hug the ground, wind and hail are sure to pound."

Minds On! Working in small groups, come up with your own weather saying. Describe a particular weather pattern by using a rhyme or catchy sentence. Share your saying with the class. ●

The weather prophets of yesterday were often accurate in their observations of

Waves such as this can be detected by satellites.

the weather. Today, we're continuing to search for accurate weather answers. One of our most valuable sources of global weather information is weather satellites. They take pictures of cloud patterns and storm systems. They also record data about winds, temperature, rainfall, water vapor, wave height, soil moisture, and snow cover.

Most satellites are either polar-orbiting or geostationary. **Polar-orbiting satellites** circle the globe traveling north to south and crossing over the poles.

Geostationary (jē′ ō stā′ shə nêr ē) **satellites** complete one orbit in the same time it takes Earth to rotate once, so they're always above the same spot on Earth's surface. The newest of these can collect information from inside hurricanes, recording wave heights, surface winds, and rainfall. Some now carry microwave sensors that can gather information even through cloud cover.

In the past, researchers haven't been able to study the section of atmosphere between 64 and 175 kilometers (about 40 and 110 miles) high. Between these heights, the atmosphere is too thin for airplanes and too thick for satellites. However, in the 1980s, the United States and Italy began an exciting new project. They developed a small satellite that could be attached to a 60-kilometer (37-mile)

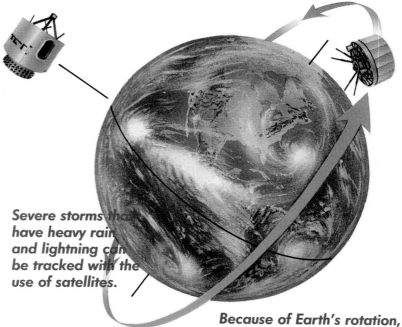

Severe storms that have heavy rain and lightning can be tracked with the use of satellites.

cable and be towed from an orbiting spacecraft to collect data. Such data are valuable in researching upper-atmospheric winds and how they affect global weather.

Because of Earth's rotation, polar-orbiting satellites cover different parts of Earth from one orbit to the next.

Geostationary satellites detect weather conditions over the same area on Earth because they rotate with Earth.

Sum It Up

The interaction of clouds, wind, water, and the land determines weather conditions. In your weather-map activities, you predicted the weather by observing these interactions and how they changed the weather. People working together around the world are able to forecast global weather patterns by tracking present weather conditions.

Critical Thinking

1. Suppose you're planning a picnic for Saturday. The Thursday weather forecast predicts that a high-pressure system will move into your area for the weekend. Should you cancel the picnic? Explain.
2. Describe the characteristics of an air mass that formed over the Sahara Desert.
3. How would an air mass that formed over New En-

gland differ from an air mass that formed over Arizona? How would they be the same?
4. What kind of weather is associated with a cold front?
5. Suppose you were asked to predict the weather for your area over the next few days. What information would you require? What instruments would you need to determine the weather conditions?

How Are Severe Storms Predicted?

When the wind begins to blow hard and big raindrops start falling, have you ever wondered how a severe storm develops? How can we tell when these storms will occur? In this lesson, you'll learn about the conditions that cause destructive storm systems. You'll also learn how to prevent damage to people and property if a disastrous storm develops in your area.

In 1988, Hurricane Gilbert raged through Jamaica. The strong winds of this hurricane smashed things in its path and ripped trees from the ground, roots and all. The towering waves it created and the rainfall it dumped turned the streets to rivers. When Hurricane Gilbert had moved on, the once-beautiful island was a jumble of twisted and tangled wreckage of demolished buildings and trees. Gilbert left 500,000 people—one fifth of the island's inhabitants—homeless.

After battering Jamaica, Hurricane Gilbert headed west and slammed into the coasts of Mexico, Texas, Louisiana, and Mississippi. In areas that received warning, people were able to prevent loss of life and protect some property. Unfortunately, lives were lost in the areas where the people had no such warning. How do you think the path of the savage storm was predicted?

In September of 1990, a tornado swept through the Illinois towns of Plainfield, Crest Hill, and Joliet with winds of 480 kilometers (about 300 miles) per hour. Nine people were pulled from their apartment buildings and thrown into a cornfield 12 meters (about 40 feet) away. This tornado created a path of destruction 26 kilometers (about 16 miles) long, injuring 90 people and killing 27 others.

Minds On! What weather conditions do you think bring on a severe storm? Where do you think it's safe to be during such a storm? Discuss these questions with a few of your classmates. Take notes in your *Activity Log* page 25. Later you can check your notes against what you learn in this lesson about severe storms. ●

Thunderstorm systems usually have high winds, but not all winds are dangerous. Without winds, all rain would fall back into the ocean, leaving only parched, barren deserts on land. Winds bring rain to the land, move warm air to cold areas, and push cool air to hot regions. Even so, winds and precipitation can combine to bring disaster to living things. What makes winds and precipitation act this way?

Hurricane Gilbert had winds that ranged from speeds of 280 kilometers (175 miles) per hour to 320 kilometers (200 miles) per hour.

Activity!

How Do Thunderstorms Form and Grow?

Tornadoes usually begin as thunderstorms, but only two percent of thunderstorms become tornadoes. Thunderstorms are quite common in many places around the world. They often provide spectacular shows of lightning and thunder. They also produce high winds, violent rain showers, and sometimes hail. Where do they most often occur? Why?

What You Need

4" strip of very thin paper
light bulb
***Activity Log* pages 26–27**

What To Do

Study the map, which shows patterns of thunderstorm frequency. This information along with the questions will help you develop a better understanding of severe thunderstorms. Write your answers in your ***Activity Log.***

Safety!

74   See the *Safety Tip* in step 5.

1. On the map find the area where you live. What's the average number of days per year your area has thunderstorms?

2. What area in the United States appears to have the fewest number of days per year with thunderstorms?

3. What general area of the United States has the most days per year with thunderstorms?

4. What is the average number of days per year you might expect thunderstorms if you were to move to Orlando, Florida?

5. Make a spiral from a 4" circle of thin paper. Hold the spiral over the hot light bulb. *Safety Tip:* Avoid contact with the hot light bulb.

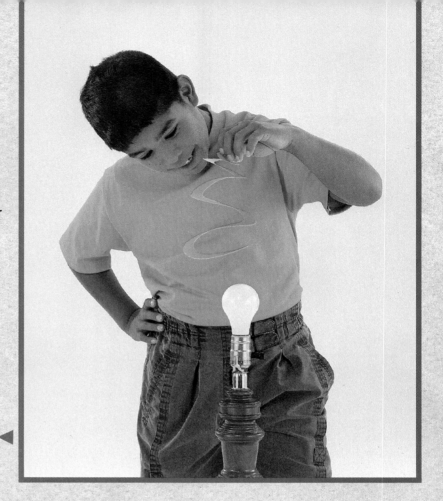

What Happened?

1. What did the paper do when you placed it above the hot light bulb?
2. What does the paper tell you about air movement? What happens to air above very warm land?

What Now?

1. Describe the atmospheric conditions in Florida and the Gulf Coast region that contribute to frequent thunderstorm activity.
2. Why do you think Nevada has so few thunderstorms each year?
3. Suppose you wished to move to a place where the threat of severe thunderstorms was extremely small. Where would you go?
4. What season of the year do you think is most likely to produce thunderstorm systems?

Inside a Thunderstorm

Lightning is caused by electrical disturbances within clouds.

In the Explore Activity on pages 74–75, you investigated some of the atmospheric conditions and interactions that cause thunderstorms to form. Thunderstorms begin when warm, humid air is forced upward rapidly. You discovered that warm air is less dense than the cooler air around it. The warmer and the more humid air is, the faster it's pushed up. As the warm air rises, the relative humidity increases until it reaches the dew point. Then the water vapor condenses to form either water droplets or ice crystals.

In a thunderstorm, rapid rising of the warm, moist air results in heavy precipitation. Sometimes hail forms. Rainfall can be so heavy that flooding results. Fortunately, high-speed winds usually push thunderclouds along, so the storm passes quickly before floods develop. Meteorologists, by knowing the conditions that cause thunderstorms to form, can often predict the development and movement of these storms. Thus, they can warn people in the path of the storms to take shelter.

When water vapor condenses or freezes, it releases heat into the air that surrounds it. This heat warms the air further, causing more uplifting. Moist air from the bottom of the system rushes in to replace the rising air. The rapidly-rising air builds a towering cumulus cloud. Air and water vapor move up and down very rapidly within this cloud.

The friction of ice crystals whizzing through the cloud creates electrical disturbances. For reasons meteorologists do not entirely understand, the cloud may produce bolts of electricity called lightning, like the photograph on page 76. Extreme heat from the lightning bolt causes the air to become very hot—up to 25,000° C (around 45,000° F). Thus, the air expands rapidly. When this sudden expansion occurs, it produces the loud noise called thunder.

Because light travels faster than sound, you see the flash of lightning before you hear the crash of thunder. If you hear the thunder five seconds after you saw the flash, the lightning struck about a kilometer and a half (about a mile) away. If the amount of time between the flash and the thunder becomes shorter, the electrical storm is moving toward you. That means it's time to take precautions. Your chance of being struck by lightning is slim. However, lightning can kill or burn the objects it strikes. The chart below will tell you how to protect yourself during a thunderstorm.

About two percent of thunderstorms produce tornadoes. Have you ever seen a tornado? How does the funnel shape spin and travel?

Thunderstorm Safety

1. Go inside if possible, but don't go into a small building that stands off by itself.
2. Avoid pipes, faucets, and electrical outlets.
3. If you can't go inside, stay away from places where you are taller than the objects around you. Don't stand on a hilltop or in an open field. If you are in the open, lie flat, even if you get wet or muddy.
4. Don't go into water. Lightning is attracted to water. Don't go out in a boat, because the boat will be taller than the surrounding water and attract the lightning.
5. Avoid anything made of metal. Lightning is attracted to metal.
6. Don't go under a tree. Head for a low spot if you're stuck in a forest.
7. A car is a safe place to be because the charge will travel through to the tires and into the ground. Be sure you aren't touching any metal parts of the car.
8. Don't use the telephone unless it's an emergency, since electricity can travel through the phone lines.
9. Lightning may be about to strike if you feel your hair stand on end. Immediately squat, lean forward, and place your hands on your knees, trying to make yourself as low to the ground as possible.

Tornadoes

A tornado is an extreme example of a wind system called a cyclone. In a cyclone, winds spiral around low-pressure centers. In the northern hemisphere these winds move counterclockwise, and in the southern hemisphere they move clockwise. Most severe storms develop in cyclonic (sī klon′ ik) wind systems. To see how air moves in a tornado, do the following activity.

This tornado in Fridley, Minnesota, caused widespread destruction.

Activity!

Make a Model Tornado

You can model the effects of a tornado.

What You Need

2 2-L plastic bottles, duct tape, dry cloth, Activity Log page 28

1. Fill 1 bottle one-third full of water.
2. Cover the mouth of that bottle with duct tape.
3. Dry the neck of the bottle.
4. Punch a hole in the center of the tape, using the pencil.
5. Place the bottles together so that the mouths touch and line up.
6. Tape the bottle necks together.
7. Have one person hold the bottles by the necks with the one containing water on top. The other person should grasp the middle of the empty bottle. Then the first person, keeping the bottles vertical, quickly swirls them in figure-eights or circles parallel to the floor. The person holding the bottom bottle should squeeze it and release to help the funnel form.

8. Set the bottles on a table, keeping the same bottle on top.
9. Notice how the motion spins the water out to the side of the bottle. In your *Activity Log*, write what you observed.

Tornadoes are powerful storms that move over land in narrow paths. Their winds are so strong they can pick up houses or smash factories. Tornadoes affect relatively small areas, but their fierce winds devastate almost everything in their path. The winds flatten buildings and hurl objects at speeds so great that straw driven by the force of a tornado's wind can penetrate wood. These winds can also pick up huge objects such as trains. Some of these objects are crushed, and others are simply carried away.

The eye, or low-pressure center of the tornado, is very calm, but it, too, can cause damage. No one had ever been in the eye of a tornado and looked up its funnel until 1928, when a Kansas farmer looked up from the door of his storm cellar just as a tornado passed over. "Everything was as still as death," he reported. "There was a strong gassy odor, and I felt as if I could not breathe." He said the eye was about 15–35 meters (about 50–100 feet) in diameter and formed a funnel at least a kilometer (about one-half mile) high.

Little can be done to avoid property damage in a tornado, but taking precautions can save lives. In 1935, the same twister hit the Texas towns of San Anselmo and Waco. The people in San Anselmo were prepared, and there, 11 people were killed and 66 injured. The people of Waco didn't think the tornado would hit their town, and so they didn't take precautions. More than 500 people were injured and 114 people lost their lives.

Tornado warnings don't come very far in advance, and they sometimes don't come at all. The path of a tornado is difficult to predict. A tornado can reduce one house to splinters and leave the one next door untouched. When meteorologists suspect that a tornado

Tornadoes appear as funnel-shaped extensions from clouds.

is forming, they warn everyone in the area to be prepared. Sometimes a tornado may approach without warning, but often you can see a tornado form.

As you may already know, tornadoes are most likely to form in the presence of thunderstorms with heavy rain or hail. How exactly does this funnel of wind develop? As the warm, humid air is forced upward within a cumulonimbus cloud, more warm air rushes in to replace the air that was forced upward.

The air that rushed in is also forced upward, and in some instances it begins to rotate. This rotating air extends beneath the cloud and may touch down toward the surface. Tornadoes can last a few minutes or as long as a few hours. They can move over the surface anywhere from 40 to 96 kilometers (25 to 60 miles) per hour, and they follow very unpredictable paths.

When a tornado has been spotted, you must take precautions immediately. The following chart tells you what to do.

Tornadoes can be tracked in order to warn people and provide them with time to use the information found in the charts. Can you imagine having a job hunting these savage storms?

Tornado Safety Procedures

If you're at home:

1. Open the windows slightly, then get away from them.
2. Go to a storm cellar if you have one, or else go to a cellar and stay underneath a staircase, mattress, or heavy piece of furniture, such as a table.
3. Don't go into a mobile home. Find shelter in a strong building.

If you're away from home:

1. Get away from the street.
2. Try to find a building to enter, but be sure to stay from windows and doors.

3. If you can't find a building, lie in a ditch and cover your head with your hands.
4. If you're at school, go to an inside hallway on the lowest floor, bend over and place your hands on your head.

Be sure to stay away from the gym, cafeteria, or any room with windows

Storm Chaser

Gathering information about tornadoes is a challenge. It's difficult to predict when they'll form or where they'll go. Once they form, they don't last very long. In fact, many meteorologists have never seen a tornado.

At the National Severe Storms Laboratory in Oklahoma City, Oklahoma, storm chasers attempt to drop weather instruments into the paths of tornadoes. Meteorologists hope to measure temperature, pressure, wind speed, and wind direction inside a tornado. Because the path of a tornado is often erratic, many tornadoes miss the instruments entirely, to the scientists' frustration.

Chasing and predicting the path of a tornado is quite difficult. Storm watchers spend most of their days waiting for a heavy thunderstorm to develop. When one does, a meteorologist uses Doppler radar to determine where tornadoes are likely to form. (You'll learn more about Doppler radar at the end of this lesson.) The storm chasers drive hundreds of kilometers to the storms that are most likely to spin out a tornado. They stay in radio contact with a meteorologist who guides them to the most-promising storm systems.

In the future, you'll be able to learn much more about tornadoes, thanks to the efforts of these daring and adventurous storm chasers.

Literature **Link**   *Night of the Twisters*

"The roaring had started somewhere to the east, then came bearing down on us like a hundred freight trains. Only that twister didn't move on. It stationed itself right overhead, making the loudest noise I'd ever heard, whining worse than any jet. There was a tremendous crack, and I felt the wall shudder behind us. I knew then our house was being ripped apart. Suddenly chunks of ceiling were falling on our heads.

We'll be buried! was all I could think.

At that moment, as plain as anything above that deafening roar, I heard my dad's voice: *The shower's the safest place.*"

Near the beginning of Ivy Ruckman's *Night of the Twisters,* Dan, his baby brother, and his best friend barely survive a severe tornado by crawling into the shower stall.

Where would you go if your home were struck by a tornado? How would you try to protect a baby? Draw a floor plan of your home. Indicate the safest places in blue, the most dangerous places in red. After your teacher returns your drawing, post it at home where all family members can see it.

Hurricanes

The cyclonic storms that cause the most widespread destruction are **hurricanes.** They are also known as typhoons in the South China Sea, cyclones in the Indian Ocean, and willy-willies in Australia. The wind speeds are usually 120 to 240 kilometers (75 to 150 miles) per hour; however, unlike tornadoes, hurricanes may be hundreds of kilometers in diameter and may last for several days. They can travel hundreds or thousands of kilometers. Hurricane Gilbert, for example, formed in a low-pressure system off the coast of Africa and traveled to the United States. In 1989, Hurricane Hugo devastated areas of Puerto Rico and other areas in the Caribbean and traveled to the southeastern United States and destroyed areas of Charleston, South Carolina.

If you even receive warning that a hurricane may strike your area, begin to take precautions. It's important to follow the advice of the authorities. Sometimes you may be told to leave the area before the storm hits. Many people have died because they ignored such warnings. If you're not advised to leave the area, use the precautions listed in the chart below.

The center of a hurricane is an area known as the eye. Within the eye, the air begins to sink because of an area of low-pressure. The air within the eye is quite calm. The eye of the hurricane can be 16–80 kilometers (10–50 miles) across. When the eye passes over an area, the wind dies and the sky may be clear and sunny. When the eye passes, fierce winds and heavy rainfall begin to pound the land and water again.

Hurricane Precautions

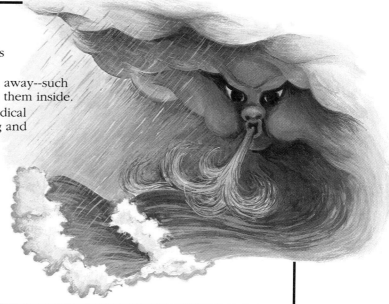

1. Tape or board up all windows. Flying debris and wind pressure can break windows.
2. Secure outdoor objects that might be blown away--such as outdoor furniture, potted plants--or bring them inside.
3. Be sure to have plenty of canned foods, medical supplies, and fresh water on hand. Shipping and receiving such items may become difficult if a storm hits.
4. Leave all low-lying coastal areas, because they're likely to be swept by high tides and storm waves.
5. Stay at home if it's on sturdy, high ground. If not, then go to the appropriate shelter.
6. Beware of the eye of the hurricane. It may produce a lull for a few minutes to half an hour. At the other side of the eye, winds can again rise very quickly.

The formation of hurricanes usually takes place over tropical oceans, at latitudes between 5° and 20°. The ocean waters are warmed in the hot, direct rays of the sun, especially in late summer and early autumn.

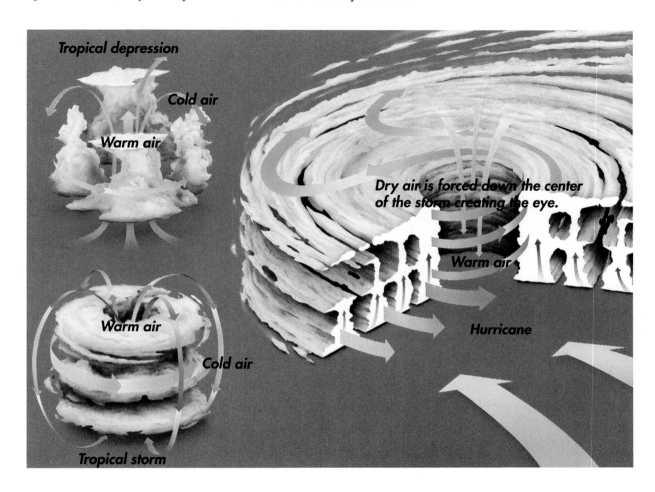

*Warm, moist air rises rapidly, creating updrafts of air and an area of very low pressure called a **tropical depression**. Surrounding air rushes into the low-pressure center, sometimes at terrific speeds. In a hurricane, winds rage around this center at speeds of more than 192 kilometers (120 miles) per hour.*

When hurricanes pass over coastal areas, the winds cause terrible destruction. Savage winds can uproot trees and level buildings. What the wind does not harm may be washed away by the high waves that develop due to high winds. These waves may be as high as 12 meters (40 feet), and the winds may carry the waves onto shore. Sweeping over the land, the waves can wash away buildings and cause great destruction. Flooding may result from the heavy rains and waves, with sometimes as much as 30 centimeters (12 inches) of water falling in a few hours.

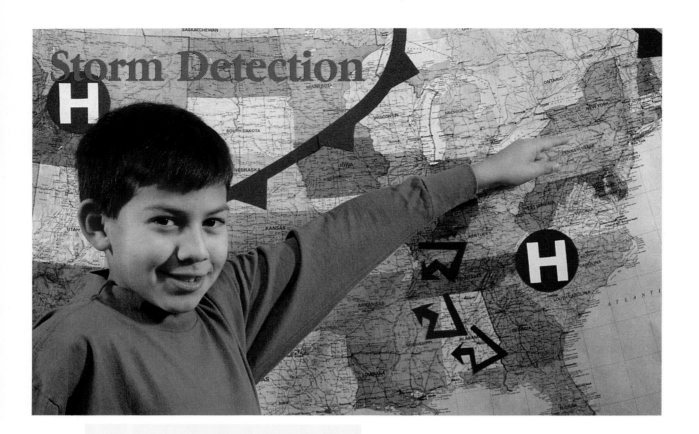

Storm Detection

Language Arts Link

Weather Reporter

Work in groups of four. Prepare and deliver a weather forecast for residents of an area where a hurricane or tornado may strike. Divide the work so that one member writes the information about the storm system, another writes up the safety procedures, and the two other members present the information to the television audience (one describing the storm system and the other the safety precautions).

Early detection and better tracking of severe storms—even tornadoes—are possible with Doppler radar. In addition to locating and tracking a storm, this advanced radar can show the direction in which a storm is moving. Different wind speeds and wind directions appear on the Doppler-radar screen in different colors. Rain, dust, and even clouds of mosquitoes can be detected by Doppler radar.

Doppler radar is used primarily by weather services. However, Doppler radar systems are being installed at airports to detect the presence of wind shear. **Wind shear** is a downward movement of cold air. This air can drop at speeds of up to 110 kilometers (about 70 miles) per hour. These downward rushes of air can rip up trees and knock airplanes out of the sky. Sometimes Doppler radar can detect these air movements in time to warn planes not to take off or land.

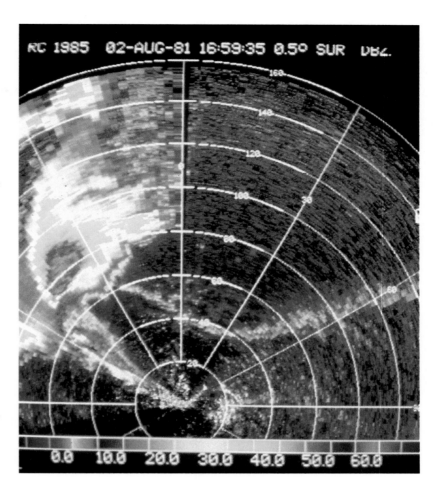

Doppler radar is one method of tracking severe storms and indicating wind shear activity.

Sum It Up

Warm, moist, rising air interacts with other elements of the atmosphere and can create severe storms. With technological advances such as Doppler radar, meteorologists can predict the approach of such storms, giving time for people to take necessary precautions. By observing the atmosphere to see how clouds, wind, temperature, and pressure systems interact, we can gain a better understanding of how tornadoes and hurricanes develop and move. With this knowledge, scientists can keep the public more well-informed and safer.

Critical Thinking

1. How does a tornado differ from a hurricane? How are they alike?

2. Suppose your favorite television program is interrupted by a severe thunderstorm warning. What's the first thing you should do?

3. Explain how a thunderstorm forms.

4. What kind of front is most often associated with tornadoes? Explain your answer.

5. Why do you think a hurricane loses its strength as it moves over land?

The Effects of Weather and Climate

As much as the weather and climate affect your life, they affect people in some parts of the world even more. For example, if a drought or a flood kills the crops in your area, you don't starve. You can go to the store and buy canned food or fresh food shipped from other areas. Most people whom you know have probably been very hungry only briefly—for only a few hours or up to a day at a time, perhaps. You yourself may know how it feels to be that hungry. Now try to imagine being hungry all the time, day after day, week after week. Many people on Earth are, as they stand on parched farmland and search the sky for signs of rain—or as they look out on flooded streets and search the sky for signs of the rain's end.

People who haven't been affected by a disas-trous tornado or hurricane can hardly imagine how thoroughly the weather can affect people's lives. Such storms can destroy a life-time's achievements in hours or even seconds. Some people, those in monsoon climates, for example, lose their crops to floods one year and to drought the next.

Lightning over city

Tropical storm

Mist over Redwood Forest National Park, California

Comparing Climates

You began observing daily weather patterns at the beginning of this unit, and you noted your observations in your weather-watch data. You also noted any weather-related choices of activities and clothing. Review your notes now, and think about the climate in your area. Try contacting your local weather bureau to obtain a report of the local climate conditions. Compare your weather-watch data with the information you receive from the weather bureau. Explain what factors affect the climate of your area. Conduct some research to find a location on Earth that has similar climate conditions to your own. Write to a school in that particular area and describe the weather and climate conditions. Ask them to respond and describe any differences they may have observed in their climate conditions as compared to yours.

The weather will always be a big factor in your life. If you understand the systems that make up our atmosphere and how they affect each other, you can predict weather and plan for it. Then you can plan your activities to take advantage of the good weather and to protect yourself from the bad.

Hailstones

Rain watering flowers

Weather and climate can affect a wide variety of areas on Earth.

GLOSSARY

Use the pronunciation key below to help you decode, or read, the pronunciations.

Pronunciation Key

a	at, bad	d	dear, soda, bad
ā	ape, pain, day, break	f	five, defend, leaf, off, cough, elephant
ä	father, car, heart	g	game, ago, fog, egg
âr	care, pair, bear, their, where	h	hat, ahead
e	end, pet, said, heaven, friend	hw	white, whether, which
ē	equal, me, feet, team, piece, key	j	joke, enjoy, gem, page, edge
i	it, big, English, hymn	k	kite, bakery, seek, tack, cat
ī	ice, fine, lie, my	l	lid, sailor, feel, ball, allow
îr	ear, deer, here, pierce	m	man, family, dream
o	odd, hot, watch	n	not, final, pan, knife
ō	old, oat, toe, low	ng	long, singer, pink
ô	coffee, all, taught, law, fought	p	pail, repair, soap, happy
ôr	order, fork, horse, story, pour	r	ride, parent, wear, more, marry
oi	oil, toy	s	sit, aside, pets, cent, pass
ou	out, now	sh	shoe, washer, fish mission, nation
u	up, mud, love, double	t	tag, pretend, fat, button, dressed
ū	use, mule, cue, feud, few	th	thin, panther, both
ü	rule, true, food	th	this, mother, smooth
u̇	put, wood, should	v	very, favor, wave
ûr	burn, hurry, term, bird, word, courage	w	wet, weather, reward
ə	about, taken, pencil, lemon, circus	y	yes, onion
b	bat, above, job	z	zoo, lazy, jazz, rose, dogs, houses
ch	chin, such, match	zh	vision, treasure, seizure

air mass: body of air that has the same properties as the region over which it develops.

atmosphere (at´ məs fîr´): a blanket of air that surrounds Earth.

barometer (bə rom´ i tər): an instrument used to measure air pressure.

cirrus cloud (sir´ əs kloud): a high, white, feathery cloud. Composed of ice crystals or supercooled water; associated with fair weather.

climate (klī´ mit): the average of all weather conditions of an area over a long period of time.

cold front: the boundary developed when a cold air mass meets a warm air mass.

condensation (kon´ den sā´ shən): process by which water vapor becomes a liquid or a solid.

condensation nuclei (kon´ den sā´ shən nü´ klē ī´): particles found in the air that provide a surface on which water molecules can condense.

Coriolis effect (kōr ē ō ləs i fekt): a phenomenon that causes a body in motion to be deflected from its initial path due to Earth's rotation.

cumulus cloud (kū myə ləs): thick, puffy cloud that develops when rising columns of moist air are cooled to the dew point.

cyanobacteria (sī´ ə nō bak tîr´ ē ə): single-celled, plant-like organisms that were the first living organisms.

cyclone (sī´ klōn): a low-pressure system in which air circulates toward the center in a counterclockwise motion in the Northern Hemisphere.

dew (dü): liquid water droplets that form on surfaces through the process of condensation.

dew point: the temperature at which condensation occurs.

doldrums (dôl´ drəmz): a windless zone at the equator.

electrolysis (i lek trol´ ə sis): the process of breaking down water into hydrogen and oxygen through the use of electricity.

evaporation (i vap ə rā´ shən): process by which a liquid becomes a gas.

exosphere (ek´ sō sfîr´): the upper zone of the thermosphere that begins at about 500–700 kilometers (about 300–420 miles) above Earth and extends into interplanetary space.

fog: a stratus cloud close to Earth's surface formed from the condensation of water vapor.

front: a boundary between air masses in which temperature and humidity differ.

geostationary satellite (jē´ ō stā´ shə ner´ ē sat´ ə līt´): a satellite that remains over a fixed area of Earth's surface.

greenhouse effect: the process by which water vapor and carbon dioxide in the atmosphere absorb and reflect infrared waves.

high-pressure center: an area of high pressure that contains cold, sinking air.

horse latitudes: regions of Earth located about 30 degrees north and south of the equator where air sinks towards the surface.

humidity (hū mid´ i tē): moisture in the atmosphere.

hurricane (hûr´ i kān´): storm that develops when warm, moist air carried by trade winds rotates around a low-pressure "eye."

infrared ray (in´ frə red´ rā): an electromagnetic wave with a wavelength between that of visible light and radio waves.

ionosphere (ī on´ ə sfîr´): the lower zone of the thermosphere that contains ions and free electrons.

jet stream: a narrow belt of wind near the tropopause that forms when warm tropical air meets cold polar air

land breeze: a circulation pattern in which warm air over water rises and is replaced by cooler air from land; occurs at night.

low-pressure center: an area of low pressure that contains warm, rising air.

meso climate (mez´ ō klī´ mit): weather conditions of a large area.

mesosphere (mez´ ə sfîr´): the coldest zone of the atmosphere that extends upward from the Earth from approximately 50 kilometers (30 miles) to about 85 kilometers (50 miles).

meteorologist (mē´ tē ə rol´ ə jist): scientist who studies storm patterns and climates in order to predict daily weather.

meteorology (mē´ tē ə rol´ ə jē): the study of weather and the forces and processes that cause it.

micro climate (mī′ krō klī′ mit): weather conditions of a small area

monsoon (mon sŭn): strong, seasonal wind that usually brings precipitation.

mountain breeze: wind that blows from the top of a mountain towards the valley below.

nimbus cloud (nim′ bəs): dark gray cloud with ragged edges from which rain or snow continually falls.

occluded front (ə klūd əd): a boundary that forms when two cool air masses merge, forcing the warmer air between them to rise.

polar easterlies (pō′ lər ēs′ tər lēz): strong winds in the polar regions formed by cold air flowing towards the equator.

polar-orbiting satellite: a satellite that orbits Earth, crossing over both poles.

polar zone: a cold climate zone that extends from the poles to 66 1/2° north and south latitudes.

precipitation (pri sip′ i tā′ shən): water that falls to Earth's surface from the atmosphere as rain, snow, hail, or sleet.

pressure (presh′ ər): force acting over an area.

prevailing westerlies (pri vā′ ling wes′ tər lēz): winds located between about 30° and 60° latitude.

radiation balance (rā′ dē ā′ shən bal′ əns): condition in which the energy Earth absorbs from the sun equals the amount of energy Earth radiates.

relative humidity: for a given volume of air at a given temperature, the ratio of the amount of water vapor present to the total amount of water vapor that that volume of air could hold.

sea breeze: a circulation pattern in which warmer air over land rises and is replaced by cooler air from water; occurs during the day.

solar radiation (sō′ lər rā′ dē ā′ shən): energy released by the sun.

source area (sôrs âr′ ē ə): the regions from which air masses are generated.

stationary front (stā′ sʜə ner′ ē frunt): a boundary that forms when either a warm front or a cold front stops moving forward.

stratosphere (strat′ ə sfîr′): the layer of the atmosphere that contains the ozone layer.

stratus cloud (strā′ təs kloud): cloud that often occurs in layers covering the whole sky, associated with light drizzle.

temperature zone (tem′ pər it zōn): a climate zone between the tropics and the polar zones where weather changes with the seasons.

thermosphere (thûr mə sfîr): the outermost layer of the atmosphere that extends from about 85 kilometers (about 51 miles) upward into space.

tornado (tôr nā′ dō): violent, whirling storm that moves in a narrow path over land.

trade winds (trād′ windz): winds formed by air rushing from the north and south toward the low-pressure area along the equator.

tropical depression (trop′ i kəl di presh′ ən): an area of low pressure in which warm, moist air rises and at great speeds can become a hurricane.

Tropic of Cancer: the boundary between the tropical and temperate zones in

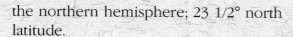

the northern hemisphere; 23 1/2° north latitude.

Tropic of Capricorn: the boundary between the tropical and temperate zones in the southern hemisphere; 23 1/2° south latitude.

tropics (trop´ iks): a climate zone lying between 23 1/2° north and south latitude that receives the greatest concentration of sunlight.

troposphere (trop´ ə sfîr´): a layer of the atmosphere nearest Earth, containing 75 percent of the gases of the atmosphere and all the weather.

valley breeze: winds that blow from a valley up a mountain slope.

warm front: a boundary that develops when a less dense, warm air mass meets a denser, colder air mass.

water cycle: the continual movement of water from one place to another and one state of matter to another.

weather (we<u>th</u>´ ər): the condition of the atmosphere over a short period of time.

wind: the movement of air from areas of high pressure to areas of low pressure.

wind-chill factor: an air temperature that reflects true air temperature combined with the chilling effects of wind speed.

wind shear (wind shîr): a downward blast of air that occurs when air is cooled through evaporation and falls rapidly because it has become denser.

INDEX

CREDITS

Macmillan/McGraw-Hill Science

FORCES AT WORK

AUTHORS

Mary Atwater
The University of Georgia

Prentice Baptiste
University of Houston

Lucy Daniel
Spindale Schools; Rutherfordton, NC

Jay Hackett
University of Northern Colorado

Richard Moyer
University of Michigan, Dearborn

Carol Takemoto
Los Angeles Unified School District

Nancy Wilson
Sacramento Unified School District

Volcanic forces in action

Macmillan/McGraw-Hill
School Publishing Company
New York   Chicago   Columbus

MACMILLAN / McGRAW-HILL

SCIENCE TURNS MINDS ON™

Suzanne O'Connell
Assistant Professor
Wesleyan University
Middletown, CT

Sidney E. White
Professor of Geology
The Ohio State University
Columbus, OH

Environmental Education:
Cheryl Charles, Ph.D.
Executive Director
Project Wild
Boulder, CO

Gifted:
Dr. James A. Curry
Associate Professor, Graduate Faculty
College of Education, University of Southern Maine
Gorham, ME

Global Education:
M. Eugene Gilliom
Professor of Social Studies and Global Education
The Ohio State University
Columbus, OH

Life Science:
Wyatt W. Anderson
Professor of Genetics
University of Georgia
Athens, GA

Orin G. Gelderloos
Professor of Biology and Professor of Environmental Studies
University of Michigan—Dearborn
Dearborn, MI

Donald C. Lisowy
Education Specialist
New York, NY

Dr. E.K. Merrill
Assistant Professor
University of Wisconsin Center—Rock County
Madison, WI

Literature:
Dr. Donna E. Norton
Texas A&M University
College Station, TX

Derrick R. Lavoie
Assistant Professor of Science Education
Montana State University
Bozeman, MT

CONSULTANTS

Assessment:
Mary Hamm
Associate Professor
Department of Elementary Education
San Francisco State University
San Francisco, CA

Cognitive Development:
Pat Guild, Ed.D.
Director, Graduate Programs in Education and Learning Styles Consultant
Antioch University
Seattle, WA

Kathi Hand, M.A.Ed.
Middle School Teacher and Learning Styles Consultant
Assumption School
Seattle, WA

Cooperative Learning:
Marcia Batcheller Harter
Director, Curriculum and Staff Development
Assistant Superintendent, Educational Services
Monterey County Office of Education
Salinas, CA

Earth Science:
David G. Futch
Associate Professor of Biology
San Diego State University
San Diego, CA

Dr. Shadia Rifai Habbal
Harvard-Smithsonian Center for Astrophysics
Cambridge, MA

Dr. Tom Murphree
Department of Meteorology, Naval Postgraduate School
Monterey, CA

Macmillan/McGraw-Hill School Division
10 Union Square East
New York, New York 10003
Printed in the United States of America

ISBN 0-02-274275-1 / 6

1 2 3 4 5 6 7 8 9 RRW 99 98 97 96 95 94 93 92

Mathematics:
Dr. Richard Lodholz
Parkway School
St. Louis, MO

Middle School Specialist:
Daniel Rodriguez
Principal
Pomona, CA

Misconceptions:
Dr. Charles W. Anderson
Michigan State University
East Lansing, MI

Dr. Edward L. Smith
Michigan State University
East Lansing, MI

Multicultural:
Bernard L. Charles
Senior Vice President
Quality Education for Minorities Network
Washington, DC

Paul B. Janeczko
Poet
Hebron, MA

James R. Murphy
Math Teacher
La Guardia High School
New York, NY

Clifford E. Trafzer
Professor and Chair, Ethnic Studies
University of California, Riverside
Riverside, CA

Physical Science:
Gretchen M. Gillis
Geologist
Maxus Exploration Company
Dallas, TX

Henry C. McBay
Professor of Chemistry
Morehouse College and Clark Atlanta University
Atlanta, GA

Wendell H. Potter
Associate Professor of Physics
Department of Physics
University of California, Davis
Davis, CA

Claudia K. Viehland
Educational Consultant, Chemist
Sigma Chemical Company
St. Louis, MO

Reading:
Charles Temple, Ph.D.
Associate Professor of Education
Hobart and William Smith Colleges
Geneva, NY

Safety:
Janice Sutkus
Program Manager: Education
National Safety Council
Chicago, IL

Science Technology and Society (STS):
William C. Kyle, Jr.
Director, School Mathematics and Science Center
Purdue University
West Lafayette, IN

Social Studies:
Jean Craven
District Coordinator of Curriculum Development
Albuquerque Public Schools
Albuquerque, NM

Special Needs:
Paulette J. Thomas, Ph.D.
Professor of Special Education
University of New Orleans
New Orleans, LA

Students Acquiring English:
Mario Ruiz
Pomona, CA

STUDENT ACTIVITY TESTERS

Alveria Henderson
Kate McGlumphy
Katherine Petzinger
John Wirtz
Sarah Wittenbrink
Andrew Duffy
Chris Higgins
Sean Pruitt
Joanna Huber
John Petzinger

FIELD TEST TEACHERS

Kathy Bowles
Landmark Middle School
Jacksonville, FL

Myra Dietz
#46 School
Rochester, NY

John Gridley
H.L. Harshman Junior High School #101
Indianapolis, IN

Annette Porter
Schenk Middle School
Madison, WI

Connie Boone
Fletcher Middle School
Jacksonville, FL

Theresa Smith
Bates Middle School
Annapolis, MD

Debbie Stamler
Margaret Tierney
Sennett Middle School
Madison, WI

CONTRIBUTING WRITER

Jay Gartrell

ACKNOWLEDGEMENTS

MOVING HEAVY THINGS by Jan Adkins. Copyright © 1980 by Jan Adkins. Reprinted by permission of Houghton Mifflin Company and Curtis Brown LTD. All rights reserved.

Reprinted with permission of Bradbury Press, an Affiliate of Macmillan, Inc. from *BURTON'S ZOOM ZOOM VA-ROOM MACHINE* by Dorothy F. Haas. Text, Copyright © 1990 by Dorothy F. Haas.

3

FORCES AT WORK

Activities!

Features

Links

Departments

FORCES AT WORK

Tug-of-war is a simple contest. Two teams hold onto a strong rope and pull in opposite directions. The winning team pulls its opponents across a marker placed on the ground between the two teams.

You've been chosen captain of a tug-of-war team. Whom do you want on your team? What determines the winner in a game of tug-of-war? What kinds of interactions between the members of each team and between the two teams are occurring? What kinds of changes in position are occurring because of these interactions?

You'll probably want to choose big, strong people for your team. But size and strength alone don't guarantee victory. The people on a tug-of-war squad all have to pull at the same time and in the same direction. Would having several very quick people on your team near the front of the rope help to get the other team moving in your direction?

When choosing a team, you may also want to consider what kind of shoes the people are wearing. Members of the soccer team who are wearing cleated shoes may be good team members, even if there are bigger people available. If the grass is slippery, soccer cleats will dig into the ground and give team members who wear them better traction.

▲ **Tug-of-war between three children on roller skates and three children in shoes**

f scientists were trying to predict the winners of a tug-of-war match, they would probably want to know the same kinds of things about the team members. A scientist might ask, "How much pulling force can each team produce? Which team has the greatest total mass? Which team can react the quickest? Are all the members of a team pulling in exactly the same direction?"

The total force applied to an object (that is, how fast and for how long the pushes or pulls are applied) and the mass of that object are factors that affect the motion of all matter on Earth. Whether you're observing the motions of a dead leaf carried by the wind or an ocean liner leaving a dock, all matter on Earth interacts with forces according to the same rules.

Forces affect all matter on Earth. In this unit, you'll learn how to identify and measure a force, how forces affect matter, and how matter behaves when forces are balanced (cancel each other out) and when they're not balanced. You'll learn to answer questions such as, "What started this object moving?" and "Why did it stop?"

In science classes, you're often asked to observe, hypothesize, col-lect and analyze data, and draw conclusions. When you do these things, you're using some of the same steps scientists use when they're doing research and experimenting. What are some steps scientists use and what do they mean?

1. **State a problem.** Many times you observe (gather information using your senses) and then ask a question about what you observe.

2. **Form a hypothesis** (hī poth´ ə sis). A hypothesis is a statement of what you think the answer to your question might be.

3. **Design an experiment.** In order for a statement to be a hypothesis, it must be able to be tested. When you design an experiment, you decide what materials and procedure you'll use to see if your hypothesis can be proved.

4. **Record and analyze data.** Any observations you make, including all measurements, must be

▲ *Tug-of-war between three children and a large boulder*

Tug-of-war between three children and an adult ▼

You'll be asked to use many of these steps as you work through the activities in science this year. Use some of these steps and try to predict the winners in some of the strange tug-of-war contests pictured on these pages.

Minds On! Work with two other people and use your *Activity Log* page 1 to practice using a scientific method process.

Look at the photo of the children having a tug-of-war contest with a boulder. State a problem question, such as "Will the children be able to pull the boulder across the line marker?" Next, write a hypothesis about what you think will happen. Then, decide how you could set up an experiment to test the hypothesis. What materials would you need, and what steps would you use? What observations would you make, and what data would need to be recorded? What conclusions do you think might be reached? ●

If you're aware of this process of science, you'll probably find yourself using some of the steps in everyday situations.

written down carefully and examined to aid you in drawing a conclusion.

5. Draw conclusions.
Once the data have all been gathered, they must be interpreted and compared with the hypothesis. Were they supported or not supported?

Usually it's not enough to have only one investigation to form a conclusion about a hypothesis. A scientist may repeat an experiment many times and may have other scientists repeat the same experiment before the results can be accepted.

Science in Literature

In the following books, you can read how forces affect the way you interact with everything around you. The forces might be tiny—have you ever felt how little force it takes to keep a canoe gliding through calm water? Or the forces might be immense—how much force do you think it would take to start an ocean liner sliding down off its wooden supports into the water? But big or small, forces are everywhere, interacting with you in lots of ways. Let's see if you can recognize some of the ways forces affect your life. Do any of the situations mentioned in the books on these two pages sound familiar?

Moving Heavy Things
by Jan Adkins.
Boston: Houghton Mifflin, 1980.

People have been lifting and carrying enormously heavy things since long before the Pyramids were being constructed. How do they do it? This book both tells and shows some little-known secrets of the moving business. Did you know that a strap around your forehead can make carrying a canoe easier? How would you knot a rope to hoist or lower an unconscious person to safety? This well-illustrated handbook makes tricky lifting problems simple. Once you've read it, you'll never mind a heavy load again.

MOVING HEAVY THINGS
JAN ADKINS

Burton's Zoom Zoom Va-ROOOM Machine by Dorothy Haas.
New York: Bradbury Press, 1990.

Have you ever dreamed of inventing a wonderful new device that would make you rich and famous? Burton invents things all through this novel, although spies lurk and enemies glare. Burton and his friends confuse all the schemes of the bad guys; Burton's family (all inventors, too) have successes and surprises of their own; and best of all, Burton's newest invention will soon be carrying kids all over the world. Of course we can't tell you much about Burton's secret invention, but here's a clue: what has skateboard wheels and rocket wings?

Other Good Books To Read ▲▲▲▲▲▲▲▲▲▲▲▲▲▲▲▲▲▲▲▲

▲ *Which Way Is Up?* by Gail Kay Haines. New York: Atheneum, 1987.

What is gravity, anyway? This book with its well-drawn pictures and simple, clear explanations will help you understand once and for all the scientific meaning for words like *up, down, weight, mass,* and many others. Even Einstein's gravitons are introduced.

▲ *The Way Things Work* by David Macaulay. Boston: Houghton Mifflin, 1988.

You'll come back to this wonderful book again and again to see how more pieces of technology work. The telephone, the computer, the jet airplane, the tape recorder, the robot—it's an endless list. Macaulay's drawings do even more than his words to make the explanations clear.

▲ *The Hidden World of Forces* by Jack R. White. New York: Dodd, Mead & Company, 1987.

Forces are at work all around us. They make heavy jets stay up, they let a knife cut a sandwich, they help us grasp a glass of water and lift it to our faces. The universe is full of matter invisible forces control. This book makes the invisible understandable.

How Do You Measure Motion?

What changes when something moves? How can you tell how fast something is moving? You can move, and objects all around you can move, but how can movement be measured? In this lesson you'll explore motion, speed, velocity, acceleration, and how to measure movement on Earth.

Who'll Be First to the Finish Line?

magine dashing into cold ocean water with a group of 1,200 swimmers. You are beginning a triathlon and will be racing with the other triathletes nonstop for almost nine hours. The finish line is 225 kilometers (about 140 miles) away! Will you be the new champion?

Triathlons are three- part races that last all day. Women and men competing in a triathlon race toward the finish line by swimming 4 kilo-

Athletes bike 180 kilometers (about 112 miles) during a triathlon.

meters (about 2.5 miles), then bicycling 180 kilometers (about 112 miles), and finally running a full marathon of 42 kilometers (26 miles). The winner is the first person to finish all three events.

Top triathletes can complete these races in about nine hours. Remember, there are three parts to a triathlon—swimming, biking, and running. How much do you think triathletes' speeds change when they switch from swimming to bicycling and from bicycling to running? Can you swim as fast as you run or run as fast as you bike?

Hundreds of swimmers begin racing at the start of a triathlon.

Minds On! Get together in groups of four to try to predict how much faster each of you can run than swim and how much faster each of you can bike than run. ●

Before entering a triathlon, athletes check the exact distances to be covered and the time the race should last. Knowing the usual speeds of other competitors in a race may help an athlete find a winning strategy. Athletes must also be certain they know the direction they should travel on the course. They can't win if they get lost!

Minds On! Scientists who study moving objects need to make accurate measurements of time and distance. Accurate time and distance measurements are also needed to determine the winner in many sports contests.

In your *Activity Log* page 2, list several different contests where the distance that something moves, rather than the time it takes, determines the winner (for example, the shot put).

In your *Activity Log*, list several sporting events in which the winner is the person who moves a measured distance in the shortest time (for example, a 100-meter dash).

During a fire drill, moving the distance from your classroom to an exit in a short period of time is important for your safety. List in your *Activity Log* several other examples of everyday tasks where time and distance are important. ●

The winner of a triathlon is the first person to cross the finish line and break the tape.

Activity!

Science Triathlon

"How long will it take us to get to the store from your house? Should we take the short cut? If you ride your skateboard, can you keep up with my bicycle?" You answer questions like these every day. You probably can estimate travel time, distance, direction, and speed very well. But sometimes you need a more exact measure of an object's speed. In this activity, you'll calculate several average speeds in a Science Triathlon.

What You Need

stopwatch
meterstick
masking tape
Activity Log pages 3–4

What To Do

1 Use masking tape to mark a starting line on the floor. Measure 10 m from the starting line and mark this as the finish line. This will be your race-course. Choose a racer, a timer, and a recorder.

2 The racer should stand a few meters behind the starting line. At the start signal, the racer begins to walk at a normal speed to the finish line. When the racer crosses the starting line, the timer times the race to the finish line.

3 Record the number of seconds it takes the racer to walk 10 m in the data table in the *Activity Log*. Repeat this "walk" 2 more times and record these data.

Add these 3 times together and divide the sum by 3 to find the average time it takes this racer to walk 10 m. Record.

4 Switch roles. Now determine how long it will take a new racer to run 10 m. The racer should run from several steps behind the starting line to the finish line when the start signal is given. Run the course 2 more times. Calculate and record the average time.

5 Switch roles again so that everyone has a new role. Complete the science triathlon with a special race. The racer must touch the toe of one foot to the heel of the other foot on each step down the 10-m racecourse. Do this 3 times. Calculate and record the average time.

What Happened?

1. Which race had the shortest average time? The longest?
2. Use the average times you calculated to find the speed for each race. You can do this by dividing the distance moved (10 m) by the average time it took to cover the distance.

$$\text{Speed} = \frac{\text{distance moved}}{\text{average time}}$$

What was the speed in m/s for the walking race? For the running race? For the walking-toe-to-heel race?

What Now?

1. How long would it take to complete a nonstop Science Triathlon by walking 10 m, running 10 m, and toe-to-heel walking 10 m? What do you predict would be the average speed for the entire 30 m? Test your prediction by calculating the total time required and then dividing the total distance of 30 m by this time. Now have one team member complete the entire race. Measure the time it takes to complete the entire race and divide 30 m by this time to find the actual average speed for this race. How does this speed compare to your calculated average speed?
2. Use your data to estimate how long it would take to walk 100 m. To run 100 m. Test your predictions.
3. Design an experiment to calculate the average speed of someone riding a bicycle. How many m/s do you think a bicycle travels?

EXPLORE

Measuring Motion

In the activity on the previous two pages, you studied several patterns of change of position. You measured the distance each racer moved and how long it took the racer to move that distance. You saw how the times changed when the racer changed his or her method of racing. You then calculated each racer's average speed.

Recall that average speed is equal to the total distance an object travels divided by the total time it takes to travel that distance. This can be written mathematically as follows.

$$\text{average speed} = \frac{\text{total distance}}{\text{total time}}$$

How does a scientist measure speed? A scientist will ask the same two questions you asked, "What distance did an object move? How much time did it take the object to move that distance?" By using these two pieces of information, a scientist calculates an object's average speed the same way you did in your Science Triathlon.

Minds On! How many ways can you tell that a car is moving? The most common way is simply to look at it. If a car is located to the left of you now, and a few seconds later it is located to your right, you know it has moved or you have moved. But do you always need to use your eyes to detect motion?

Imagine you're sitting in a car with a blindfold over your eyes. Could you tell if the car started to move? What would you feel if the car started off very quickly, turned a corner, or came to a sudden stop? Would the sound of the car's engine be different when it started moving? If the car's windows were open, would the air hitting your face feel different when the car started to move? What are all the different ways that you can sense motion? ●

The average speed of a runner is equal to the total distance run divided by the total time it takes to run that distance.

Long before there were baseball pitchers throwing fastballs or astronomers studying the motions of planets, people wanted to know how things moved. Humans living 100,000 years ago were motion experts. Hunters heaving a rock or a spear at wild game needed an accurate throw to get food.

Today's physicists are just as interested as those early hunters in how things move. **Physicists** (fiz´ ə sists) are scientists who study the structure and interactions of matter, as well as the changes in position that matter undergoes.

Matter is the "stuff" that makes up everything in the universe. Skyscrapers, ants, planets, and pollen grains are all composed of matter. Physicists have found that matter moves in predictable ways.

Physicists often measure the motion of matter, or speed, in meters per second. Everyday measures of speed such as how fast a car or airplane is traveling are given in kilometers per hour in most of the world. (A kilometer is 1,000 meters, about 0.62 mile.) Only one country, the United States, still uses the English units of inch, foot, yard, and mile to measure distance. When using English units, speed is usually given in feet per second or miles per hour.

Travel Agents—Time, Distance, and Direction Experts!

Physicists aren't the only people who need to be motion experts. Travel agents also need to be motion experts.

"What's the best way to make the following trip? I need to fly from Durham, North Carolina, early Wednesday and arrive in Tulsa, Oklahoma, by 11:00 A.M. Wednesday. Then, I need to be in Oklahoma City the next day for a 2:00 P.M. meeting. Should I rent a car at the airport or fly from Tulsa to Oklahoma City?"

Travel agents answer questions like this every day. Their job is to find the fastest, most convenient, and most economical means of travel for people who travel for business or for fun. They must have a knowledge of time, distance, and direction.

Travel agents spend much of their time working with computers. Their computers link them with airline, train, and hotel information networks so they can give their clients several different travel options.

When they're not working on their computers, travel agents may be taking free trips to learn about vacation resorts. They're working during these trips, but they also get to do some sightseeing!

Matter in Motion

Scientists investigating an object's motion will also want to know in what direction the object is moving. When both the speed and direction of an object are known, the object's **velocity** (və los´ i tē) can be defined.

Physicists are careful to distinguish between speed, which describes how fast an object is moving, and velocity, which describes both speed and direction. Nonscientists often use velocity and speed incorrectly to describe the same motion. For example, a car traveling on a curvy road

In 1990, the winning Indy race car traveled about 807 kilometers (500 miles) in 2.69 hours.

In 1911, the winning Indy race car traveled about 807 kilometers (500 miles) in 6.67 hours.

with its cruise control set at 88 kilometers (about 55 miles) per hour would stay at a constant speed of 88 kilometers per hour. However, this car's velocity would vary, though its speedometer always read the same. The car's velocity changes every time the car changes direction on a curve.

How do you use measures of speed and distance in everyday life? Knowing your speed and the distance you need to travel allows you to estimate how much time it will take to reach a certain destination. Suppose you wanted to travel from Atlanta, Georgia, to Indianapolis, Indiana, to see the famous Indy 500 automobile race. How long would it take to get there in a car traveling at an average speed of 80 kilometers (about 50 miles) per hour?

By checking a map, you learn that Atlanta and Indianapolis are about 800 kilometers (500 miles) apart—the same distance that the Indy 500 cars will go during the race. To calculate the time you would need to allow for travel, you divide the distance you will go by your average speed: 800 kilometers ÷ 80 kilometers per hour = about 10 hours. It would take you a bit more than ten hours of driving to complete this trip even if you did not stop for food or fuel.

How long would it take the winning Indy 500 race cars to travel the same distance, about 800 kilometers, at their top speed? The answer changes every year. Race cars are constantly being redesigned to go faster while maintaining safety. Sometimes bad weather or accidents slow the average speed of the race cars. In 1911, the first year that the Indy 500 was held, the winning car averaged about 120 kilometers (about 75 miles) per hour. In 1990, the winning car averaged 300 kilometers (186 miles) per hour. Use what you've learned about speed and distance to calculate how long it took these cars to complete the race!

Cars like this race about 807 kilometers (500 miles) at the Indy 500 race.

Have you ever stopped at the top of a steep hill, then coasted down on a skateboard or bicycle? Were you going at the same speed at the bottom of the hill as you had been near the top? Describe how your speed changed as you went down the hill.

The moving objects you've studied so far in this unit have all been moving at a constant speed. How can you tell for sure if you're moving at a constant speed or if your speed changes? One way to do this is to measure your change in position (how far you move) during a standard period of time (such as one second). To see how this works, do the Moving Marbles activity below.

The girl on the bike is pedaling along at a steady rate on flat ground. Her average speed is five meters per second. If her speed is constant, she'll travel five meters in the first second, another five meters in the next second, another five meters in the following second, and so on until she puts on the brakes to slow down or pedals faster to speed up. An object traveling at **constant speed** moves the same distance during each second of travel.

But what if the girl on the bicycle stops at the top of a steep hill? How will her speed change when she starts down? In the first second, she moves a short distance down the hill. She isn't moving fast—only one meter per second. During the next second, she picks up speed and is moving at two meters per second. If the hill flat-

Activity!

Moving Marbles!

What You Need

2 metersticks, masking tape, 2 school books, stopwatch, marble, *Activity Log* page 5

Tape 2 metersticks together so they form a V-shaped track as shown. Place this track on a long table or desk. Prop the first 10 cm of the track up on 2 school books. Place the marble in the higher end of the track. Let it roll down the track while your partner uses a stopwatch to call out when 1 s has passed, 2 s have passed, and 3 s have passed. Measure the distances when your partner calls out the times and record in your *Activity Log*. Repeat 2 more times. Average the distances the marble moved during each of the seconds. Record these data in your *Activity Log.* Subtract the average distance moved at 1 s from the average distance moved at 2 s. Subtract the average distance moved at 2 s from the average distance moved at 3 s. Record these numbers. Did your marble move the same average distance during each of the seconds?

tened out at this point, she could continue to coast at two meters per second for a while. But since she's on a steep hill, her speed continues to increase. After several more seconds, she's moving at six meters per second. Coasting down a steep hill on a bike is an example of acceleration. Scientists define **acceleration** as the rate of change of an object's velocity.

You saw in the Moving Marbles activity that the marble moved different distances each second. It was accelerating. How might you tell that the girl riding the bike down the hill was accelerating?

You probably think of something speeding up when you hear the term acceleration. This is only partly true. Scientists define all changes in speed or direction as acceleration. An object that is slowing down has negative acceleration. This is why scientists use the term velocity very carefully. Remember, velocity describes both the speed and the direction of a moving object. When an object changes directions, its velocity changes even if its speed does not.

In this lesson, you won't be asked to calculate an object's acceleration. However, it's important for you to be able to answer yes or no to the question, "Is this object accelerating?"

| 6 m/s | 5 m/s | 4 m/s | 3 m/s | 2 m/s | 0 m/s 1 m/s 1 m/s | 2 m/s 3 m/s | 3 m/s | 3 m/s | 3 m/s |

You've learned about motion, speed, velocity, and acceleration of humans. What about the animals on Earth? Animals can reach amazing speeds and achieve rapid acceleration. Here are some maximum speeds of living organisms. How do the maximum speeds of animals compare with the maximum speeds of humans?

Amazing Motion in the Animal Kingdom

Organism/Conditions	Speed (kilometers per hour)
homing pigeon - level flight, no wind	152
hummingbird - level flight	37
himmingbird - power dive	103
African elephant	39
African rhinoceros	48
cheetah	71
greyhound	64
California sea lion - under water	16
Pacific bottlenose porpoise	30
racehorse	64
dragonfly	97
human - running short distance	36
human - running 1.6 kilometers (1 mile)	24
human - swimming	6.75
human - riding a bicycle	68

Just in Time

Do you sometimes use interesting expressions about how fast things are moving? These expressions often contain comparisons to animals. How slow is "a snail's pace"? How fast does a deer run? The actual speeds of objects used in some expressions like these are given.

Write a funny story that uses all (or most) of these sayings about speed. Feel free to invent your own expressions of speed for the story, too!

A stopwatch can be used to time the motion of elephants, cheetahs, ostriches, and swimmers.

Expression			Speed - in kilometers per second, minute, or hour
"slow as a turtle"			0.8 km/h
"quick as a fox"			48 km/h
"move at a snail's pace"			5.0 cm/minute
"faster than a speeding bullet"			275 m to 320 m/s
"a blazing fastball"			165 km/h
"a mile a minute"			96.5 km/h
"escape velocity"			40,000 km/h
"runs like a deer"			56 km/h
"like a streak of lightning"			300,000 km/s
"like the speed of sound"			335 m/s

Sum It Up

In this lesson, you've learned how to determine the speed of an object. When you calculated speed in your Science Triathlon, you divided the distance the racer moved by the time it took him or her to move that distance. You discovered, too, how speed differs from velocity; velocity includes the object's direction of motion. If an object's velocity is changing, then the object is accelerating. Speed, velocity, and acceleration describe the patterns of change of motion by showing various kinds of change in an object's position.

Critical Thinking

1. Why is it called *average* speed?
2. What's the difference between speed and velocity?
3. What's your average speed if it takes you 30 minutes to walk to a friend's house that is two kilometers away?
4. Think about riding in a car from your home to school. How would you determine your average speed? When would the car accelerate?
5. Can speed ever be negative? What about acceleration? If so, give an example.

The release of energy from inside Earth caused forces to occur
that led to the eruption of Mount St. Helens on May 18, 1980.

What Is Force?

Mount St. Helens before the May 18, 1980 eruption

Every day you experience several different forces, but you may not call them forces. You may say, "This book was pushed across the desk," or "I pulled my brother to school in a wagon." In this lesson, you'll learn about several kinds of forces and what causes them to occur.

Mount St. Helens after the May 18, 1980 eruption

Suddenly, the north side of Mount St. Helens rippled like water. Rocks and ice crashed down the sides of the volcano into the lake below. An enormous blast of scorching gas filled the air with ash traveling faster than the speed of sound. Two geologists flying over the mountain witnessed an amazing release of energy from inside Earth.

This release of energy caused tremendous forces to occur. In a matter of minutes, these forces caused the eruption and landslides that tore off the top 400 meters (about 1,300 feet) of Mount St. Helens. Its snow-covered peak was scarred by a crater 600 meters (about 2,000 feet) deep and 2,100 meters (about 6,900 feet) wide. A deadly blanket of hot, smoking ash soon covered a huge area around the mountain. Ash blocked out the sun in nearby towns, making noon as dark as night. The blast tossed 18-wheel logging trucks into the air, splintered ancient trees, and knocked down whole forests.

Volcanic eruptions, floods, earthquakes, hurricanes, tornadoes—in all of these spectacular events, matter is pushed and hurled about. These events unleash forces that shape and reshape Earth. Natural disasters are easy to study because they make obvious changes on Earth. However, scientists don't fully understand all the other forces shaping our planet.

Until the 1960s, few scientists had studied the enormous forces that occur within Earth that form mountains, move continents, and produce ocean basins. These forces are hard to study because the changes they cause occur deep underground over a very long period of time.

The landmasses we call continents don't appear to be moving, but they are. Geologists, scientists who study the structure of Earth, have discovered that continents and oceans float like rafts on top of 15 huge plates of rock that cover Earth's surface. Plates can move from one to ten centimeters per year, carrying entire continents or ocean basins with them. The forces required to move these plates are enormous. Scientists are still investigating how these forces are produced.

Where different plates collide, mountains are pushed up, volcanoes form, and earthquakes occur. Old areas of Earth's surface are sometimes buried deep under other plates, and new land forms in rifts or cracks between the plates. The eruptions of Mount St. Helens and the volcanic mountains in the northwestern United States are examples of what happens in an area where two plates are colliding.

Of course, not every force in the world is strong enough to move mountains. To feel different strengths of forces, do the Try This Activity on the next page.

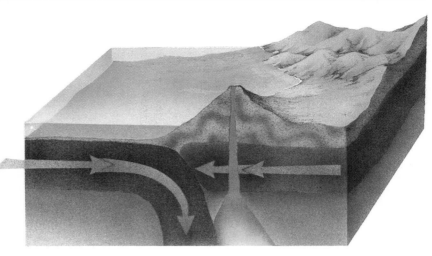

When two plates collide, one plate can slide under the other. Part of the plate material moves down and melts. This melted material rises and when it reaches the surface, it produces a volcano.

Plates are blocks of Earth's crust and upper mantle.

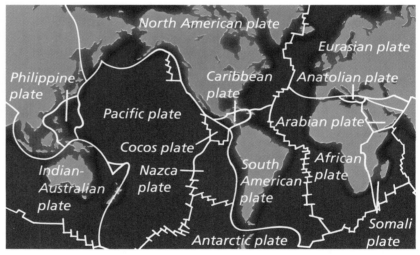

North American plate

Eurasian plate

Philippine plate

Caribbean plate

Anatolian plate

Pacific plate

Arabian plate

Cocos plate

Indian-Australian plate

Nazca plate

South American plate

African plate

Antarctic plate

Somali plate

TRY THIS

Activity!

Experience a Force

Now you can experience a force.

What You Need
your hands, hand lotion, *Activity Log* page 6

Place your hands together lightly. Rub your hands back and forth quickly. Is it hard to move them this way? How do they feel when you stop?

Press your hands together tightly. Rub them back and forth. How do they feel when you stop?

Apply hand lotion to your hands. Press your hands together tightly and rub them back and forth. Write your observations in your *Activity Log*.

Activity!

Slipping and Sliding

In this activity, you'll pull an object across a table to see if changing the surface between the object and the table changes the force needed to move it across the table.

What You Need

smooth, level desk or table
3 small school books (all the same size)
2 self-sealing plastic food bags
2-m length of string
2 pencils
roller skate (optional)
sheet of sandpaper (at least as wide as the book covers)
masking tape
Activity Log pages 7–8

What To Do

1 Place 2 books in 1 bag and 1 book in the other bag. Seal the bags. Place both bags on a smooth table and tie the string around them. Leave 1 m of string between the bags. Move the bags until the string between them is tight and the bag containing 1 book is hanging off the edge of the table.

2 Let go of the bag hanging off the table. Record your observations in your *Activity Log*. Repeat this step 2 more times. What do you observe?

3 Tape a sheet of sandpaper onto the table, rough side up. Place the bag containing 2 books on top of it and let the bag containing 1 book hang off the table. Release the bag hanging off the table. Record your observation in your *Activity Log*. Repeat this step 2 more times.

4 What would happen if the books were sliding across the table on rollers? Write your prediction in your *Activity Log*. Place 2 pencils underneath the bag holding the 2 books. Let the bag holding 1 book pull them across the table. Record your observation in your *Activity Log*.

What Happened?

1. What supplied the force to slide the books across the table?

2. What had to happen for the books to slide across the table?

3. In what ways do the books slide differently if you set them on sandpaper? On pencils? Why do you think this is the case?

4. Are any forces affecting the sliding books besides the pull of the book?

What Now?

1. Can you think of other ways to make it easier to slide the books across the table? What would happen if you put them on a small cart or a roller skate? Test one of your ideas.

2. Can you think of a toy or a game that uses a sliding object? Describe the game. Could you still play the game if the sliding object were coated with rubber cement? Coated with oil?

EXPLORE

What Can We Find Out About Forces?

A **force** is a push or a pull that one object exerts on another object. It takes a force to start a lump of matter moving, stop it from moving, or change its velocity.

Friction is a force that opposes motion between the surfaces of two objects that are touching. Friction depends on the kinds of surfaces between the two objects and on the amount of force pressing the two objects together. Friction causes moving objects to slow down and eventually stop. It always acts in the direction opposite to the movement of an object.

Friction also occurs between two touching objects that are just sitting still. In this case, the frictional force between the two objects is just great enough and in the right direction to balance out any other forces that are acting on the objects at that time. The total force on the two objects is zero, and the objects won't start to move.

The more friction that exists between the bow and the violin strings, the easier it is to set the strings in motion.

There's no acceleration. The more force pressing two objects together, the more friction there is between those two objects.

You've done two activities that demonstrated how friction affects moving objects. When you rubbed your hands together hard in the activity on page 27, you felt your palms get hot. Friction produces heat. In the Explore Activity, you found it's harder to pull a book across a piece of sandpaper than across a smooth table. The rough surface of the sandpaper increased the friction between the book and the table. The book moved more slowly across the sandpaper than across the smooth table. These activities demonstrated two of the main effects of friction: warming up moving surfaces and slowing down moving objects. Now do the following activity to use friction to make music.

Activity!

Friction Music

Ben Franklin made music with friction. You can try his experiment.

What You Need

drinking glass with stem (half full of water), lemon juice, *Activity Log* page 9

Make sure the glass you use has no dents or chips on the rim. Hold the glass firmly on the table with one hand. Wet one of the fingers of your other hand and rub it around the rim of the glass in a circular motion. As you rub around the rim, press on it very gently at

first. Slowly increase the pressure until the glass produces a clear, bell-like tone. *Safety Tip:* Hold the glass steady, and don't press so hard that you break it!

If you have trouble making the glass ring, wash your hands with soap and rinse them with water to remove any soap film. Dipping the tips of your fingers in a few drops of lemon juice will also help to increase the force friction between your fingers and the rim of the glass.

After you can make the glass ring, change the amount of water. Does the sound change when you raise or lower the water level? Can you change the sound by rubbing faster or slower? By pressing harder or softer? Can you and your class play a tune? Record your answers in your *Activity Log.*

Music/Art Link

Friction Can Make Beautiful Music

Sounds produced by the friction of two objects rubbing together can be irritating or pleasing. Squeaking chalk across a blackboard makes people cringe. Crickets attract their mates by rubbing their front wings together to make chirping sounds. But rubbing a bow across the strings of a violin or strumming a guitar string can start the strings vibrating and make music.

The quality and amount of sound produced when two objects rub together partly depends on the amount of friction between them. Recall that when you dipped your fingers in lemon juice you increased the friction between your fingers and the glass. Bows for stringed instruments are made by attaching hairs from the tail of a horse to a wooden bow. Horsehairs are smooth. Violinists rub rosin on the hairs of their bow to increase the friction between the bow and the strings. The more friction

there is between the bow and the strings, the easier it is to set the strings in motion when the bow slides across them. The vibrations of the violin's strings make the musical sounds you hear.

In 1763 Benjamin Franklin invented an instrument called the glass harmonica. It consisted of glass bowls mounted on a spindle that was turned by a foot pedal. By moving his fingers from one bowl to the next, he could play complete musical pieces.

Friction and the Environment

Reducing friction is good for the environment and good for your wallet.

What would you do if you learned a simple way to reduce friction that would cost you nothing, would help decrease air pollution, and could save money? Would you be willing to try it?

All you need to do is to get the automobile owners you know to inflate the tires on their cars to the maximum safe pressure recommended.

Badly underinflated tires produce more friction and increase the amount of gasoline a car burns by as much as six percent.

In the United States, manufacturers are required by law to produce cars that get an average of 44 kilometers (about 28 miles) per gallon of gasoline. Since most people drive their cars about 24,000 kilometers (about 15,000 miles) per year, car owners buy about 2,070 liters (about 545 gallons) of gas a year at a cost of about $818.

Underinflated tires produce more friction than properly inflated tires and make it harder for the car to move along the road. When tires are underinflated, they wobble from side to side. This increases the friction between the road and the tire. The extra friction will cause fuel mileage to drop to 41 kilometers (about 26 miles) per gallon. This may not sound like a big change, but it means that the driver will have to spend about $52 per year more to drive the same distance. Because the car is burning more gasoline, it will also put an additional 665 pounds of CO_2 (carbon dioxide) into the atmosphere. CO_2 is one of the "greenhouse gases" that scientists are studying to see if they produce long-term changes in Earth's climate.

Improperly inflated tire.

Properly inflated tire.

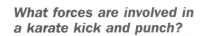

What forces are involved in a karate kick and punch?

Minds On! What is giving a push or a pull in these pictures? Forces are acting in every case. How many pushes and pulls can you identify for each of the pictures? ●

What forces are involved in a golf swing?

What forces are involved when a child on a swing drags both feet on the ground?

The diver is falling toward the water because of the force of gravity.

Forces in Your World

You need to know two things to determine the effect of a force on an object—the direction of the force (which way it's pushing or pulling) and how strong the force is (its magnitude).

Why does a diver jumping off a ten-meter platform fall toward the water? To answer, you need to know all the forces acting on the diver. What's the direction of the force? How strong is it? Are there any other forces acting at the same time?

One force you'll need to consider is gravity. Gravity is the force that pulls us toward the ground and holds water in the bathtub. Gravitational forces hold the moon in orbit around Earth and hold the planets in orbits around the sun.

The diver falls toward the water because gravity is a force acting between her and the water and because there is no longer a force pushing up on the diver, as there was when she was standing on the diving platform. **Gravity** is a pulling force that every object exerts on every other object. The force of gravity depends on the masses of the objects and the distance between them. The greater mass an object has, the more pulling force of gravity it will exert. Earth has more mass than the diver, so it exerts a greater pulling force of gravity on the diver than the diver exerts on Earth. Therefore the direction of pull of the diver is toward Earth. Gravity always pulls objects smaller than Earth toward the center of Earth. If Earth has more mass than an object, it will exert a greater force of gravity on the smaller object than the smaller object will exert on Earth. So, for any falling object less massive than Earth, including the diver, "down" is the answer to the question "What direction?"

As the distance between two objects

decreases, the pull of gravity between them increases. As the distance increases, the pull of gravity decreases.

You've probably been asked how much you weigh. You most likely answered in pounds. You may recall that scientists define weight as the force of gravity acting on a mass on Earth's surface. The unit of force used by scientists is the newton, and the symbol for newton is N. Weight is a measure of force, so it's expressed as newtons.

You need a measuring device to tell how strong a force is. Scientists often use spring scales to measure the magnitude of a force. A medium-sized apple hanging in a tree pulls down on the tree limb with a force of about one newton. The diver shown is being pulled downward by gravity with a force equal to her weight in newtons.

Scientists have tested the strength of Earth's gravity and found it to be just about the same all over the world. So anywhere on our planet that the diver performs, Earth's gravity will pull her down with about the same magnitude of force. But gravity will pull a person of greater mass with a greater pull.

Identifying the direction and strength of gravity, the main force acting on the diver, is easy. But answering the physicist's last question— "Are any other forces acting?"—is trickier. There are always several forces acting on all matter in motion near the surface of Earth. Many are hard to notice. However, one force always should be accounted for—the force of friction.

There's friction between the diver and the air. The diver's body pushes the air out of the way as she falls toward the water. This type of friction is called air resistance or drag. Do the Try This Activity to discover some properties of air resistance.

TRY THIS
Activity!

Design another experiment with the cardboard to feel the force of air resistance. You may wish to cut or fold it. Write directions for your new experiment and the results you get in your *Activity Log.*

Air Resistance

You can feel friction between the air and an object.

What You Need
1 large piece of stiff cardboard
Activity Log page 10

Stand in a clear area and hold the piece of cardboard away from you. Swing it through the air. Did you feel the resistance of the air against the cardboard?

A ir resistance isn't a strong force for divers leaping from a ten-meter platform. Most divers never notice friction between themselves and the air. Astronauts, however, are especially interested in friction between the skin of their spacecraft and Earth's atmosphere.

Friction heats the skin of satellites reentering the atmosphere to several thousand degrees. Spacecraft returning to Earth must have heat shields. Otherwise, the heat generated by friction with the air would damage or destroy the spacecraft and its contents.

Heat-resistant tiles cover the fuselage of this spacecraft. These tiles shield the spacecraft from the heat generated by friction as the spacecraft reenters Earth's atmosphere.

Dynamic Diving on the Moon

If astronauts someday build a swimming pool on the moon, a diver could do much fancier dives than are possible here on Earth! On the moon, divers would fall ten meters from the platform to the water much more slowly than on Earth. With more time before hitting the water, spectacular dives would be easy! How is this possible?

G ravity exerts about the same amount of force everywhere on Earth's surface, but other places in the universe have different amounts of gravity. On the moon, the force of gravity is only one-sixth as strong as on Earth. The force of gravity is proportional to the mass of the objects. Earth is about six times more massive than the moon. Since the pull of the moon's gravity is weaker than the pull of Earth's gravity, falling objects accelerate toward the moon's surface more slowly than they would on Earth. The moon doesn't have an atmosphere, so air resistance wouldn't be a problem, either.

Can you think of other amazing feats you could do on the moon? Can you think of things that might be harder or more awkward to do on the moon?

Do You Have To Be Touching To Push or Pull?

You touch directly most of the things that push and pull you around. When you shove a refrigerator or zoom off on roller skates, you have a physical link to the thing you are pulling or pushing. You know gravity is a force that works without touching. Is it possible to exert another type of force without touching something? The Moving Magnets activity below will help you discover an answer.

This train floats above the track due to the magnetic force from the train and the magnetic force from the track. The train "floats" because these magnetic forces push each other away. Is there a lot of friction between the train and the track?

TRY THIS Activity!

Moving Magnets

What You Need
3 ring magnets, wooden pencil, *Activity Log* page 11

Stick the pencil through the hole in one of the magnets. Hold the pencil so the sharp end is pointing toward the ceiling. Place another magnet on the point of the pencil, and slowly lower it toward the bottom of the pencil. Are the magnets exerting a force on each other? Describe the force you feel. Remove the top magnet, but don't take the bottom magnet off the pencil. Turn the top magnet over and put it back on the pencil so its opposite side faces the bottom magnet. Slowly lower the top magnet as before. Do the magnets exert a force on each other this time? Is it the same kind of force you felt before? Describe the differences in the forces you feel in your *Activity Log*. Can magnets exert a force when they aren't touching each other? How can you tell? Can magnets exert both a push and a pull? What determines whether magnets push against each other or pull apart? Experiment by putting 3 magnets on the same pencil in different ways. Can you make 2 magnets "float" above the bottom magnet? Sketch the positions of the magnets when they are floating or sticking together. Are there similarities or differences between the magnetic forces and the force of gravity?

37

Friction Forces: Design and Engineering Aspects

Friction makes things hard to move. Transportation engineers and designers develop oils and lubricants to reduce friction in car engines and other moving parts. They also use wind tunnels to test the friction between high-speed air and car bodies. Streamlined vehicles slip through the air with less friction, so they use less gasoline and therefore cause less air pollution.

Transportation engineers and designers also do research on ways to increase friction! The force produced by the engine of a car couldn't push the car down the road without some friction between the tires and the road. Drivers find that they need more friction when they try to climb a steep hill on ice or stop quickly on badly worn tires. Think of what happens when you try to walk fast or run on ice.

Engineers test new car designs in wind tunnels to determine the amount of air resistance between the car and the air.

Literature Link

Moving Heavy Things

"The cunning ways friction has been reduced would please the great Leonardo da Vinci. Monument builders move marble, granite, and slate blocks on their bases with ice cubes, adjusting positions and then allowing the unwieldy weights to melt into place. Sheet metal workers move half-ton flats of sheet copper and stainless steel by levering them up and rolling baseballs beneath them."
(excerpted from *Moving Heavy Things* by Jan Adkins)

What heavy things might you want to move more easily by reducing friction? Think of a very heavy thing, and draw a way to move it that reduces friction to a minimum. Show your drawing to a classmate. Have him or her write a sentence telling what's happening in your drawing.

Ancient Egyptian sleds, modern dog sleds, and modern snowmobiles all use runners to reduce the friction between the sled and the ground.

GLOBAL PERSPECTIVE

The Evolution of Sleds

The first vehicle designed by humans wasn't a cart with wheels, but a sled. About 10,000 years ago, people built sleds consisting of platforms with runners.

Sleds allowed people to drag heavier loads than they could carry. Egyptians used sleds to move giant stones for the pyramids. They sometimes greased the runners for easier sliding. What force were they trying to reduce?

The Inuit (in' ü it) people are Native Americans who live in snow-covered northern Alaska and Canada. They transport heavy loads such as the bodies of seals, whales, and other wildlife to their villages.

Inuit designers over 1,000 years ago designed an efficient sled that could be pulled by dog teams. It's lightweight, has low-friction runners, and can carry heavy loads over snow and ice. The basic design is still in use. One thing has changed, however. Snowmobiles, rather than dogs, provide the force to pull many Inuit sleds today!

Sum It Up

In this lesson, you've learned that forces push and pull matter and that motion occurs only if the position of an object is changed. Friction acts to oppose motion and causes objects to slow down or stop. Another familiar force is gravity. Objects exert gravitational force on all other objects. The strength of the force of gravity between any two objects depends on their masses and the distance between them. Friction, gravity, and other forces interact and are important considerations for transportation designers and engineers, who work on new means of moving matter from one place to another.

Critical Thinking

1. What is friction? Is the force of friction greater between two children on a sled and the snow or between only one of the children on the same sled and the snow? Why?

2. Would it be possible to walk if there were no friction? Explain.

3. What forces are acting on a ball just after it is thrown?

4. Explain why astronauts weigh less on the moon.

5. Why is the pull of gravity on the moon less than the pull of gravity on Earth?

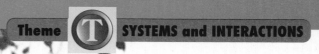

Can an Object Start or Stop Moving Without Help From a Force?

Starting and stopping, slowing down and speeding up—you probably experience these actions every day. Do you ever wonder what causes an object to start or stop moving? What might happen if people couldn't start or stop moving when they needed to? In this lesson, you'll find out how objects at rest can be made to move and how objects in motion can be made to stop.

Wildfire gallops onto the racecourse carrying her jockey. They are competing in a steeplechase—a contest of fence-jumping and speed. The horse and jockey who clear all the fences in the shortest time will become champions.

Wildfire approaches the first barrier—a fence 1.5 meters (about 5 feet) tall. The jockey gives a slight nudge to the horse's side. The horse springs forward, jumping the fence with room to spare. They make a slight turn and line up for the next hurdle.

Wildfire changes her stride as horse and jockey approach the next barrier, a wall with two rails on top. The horse is a little off balance and senses she cannot make a clean jump. Will she hit the rail and fall?

The jockey urges her to hurdle the wall, but Wildfire refuses. At the last possible moment she drops her head, braces her front legs, and stops short of the wall, uninjured.

But her jockey does not stop. He keeps moving straight toward the barrier, flies over Wildfire's lowered head, and sails over the wall alone. Gravity pulls the jockey toward Earth's center, and he lands with a thump. Luckily, he's not badly hurt, but he and Wildfire won't win today's race.

Spills like these often happen during steeplechases. Why do objects keep going forward when the platforms they are riding on stop? Do the activity on the right to experience this.

You've just read about a jockey clearing the fence even when the horse stopped, and you've observed the motions of water balloons after they left your hand when you stopped running. How are these situations similar?

Both the jockey and the water balloons were riding on a moving platform (the horse and your hand). Both platforms were moving forward in a straight line. The horse was galloping toward the fence and you were running toward the finish line. Each of the platforms suddenly stopped. What happened to the motion of the jockey and the balloons?

If the horse stops moving, what happens to the jockey?

TRY THIS

Activity!

Moving Balloons

You'll use balloons to test motion. What can you discover?

What You Need

masking tape, meterstick, 2 balloons, water, *Activity Log* page 12

Mark a "start" and "finish" line with masking tape on the pavement 10 m apart. Tape a "warning" line 1 m in front of the finish line. Fill the balloon with water and tie a knot in the open end. Hold it by the knotted end out to the side of your body at shoulder height. At the start line, begin to run toward the finish line at a constant speed. Let go of the balloon directly over the warning line. Where did the balloon hit the ground?

Get another water-filled balloon. Set the balloon in the palm of your hand. Go to the start line, raise the balloon away from your body to shoulder height and run down the course again. This time, stop suddenly just as you reach the warning line. What happens to the motion of the balloon? Record your observations in your *Activity Log*.

EXPLORE Activity!

Jet Racing Cars

You've seen that if matter is moving, it tends to keep on moving—like the jockey and the water balloons. If matter isn't moving, it will tend to stay where it is—at rest. How can you make matter that is at rest start moving?

What You Need

balloon-powered jet car
4 nickels
meterstick
lightweight cardboard
** 8 1/2" x 11"**
masking tape
scissors
***Activity Log* pages 13–14**

What To Do

1 Make a balloon inflation gauge by cutting the sheet of cardboard into a "U" shape. The opening of the "U" should be 12 cm wide.

2 Mark a starting line by sticking the masking tape on a smooth, level floor or table surface 2 m long. Place the meterstick so that one end is even with the starting line.

3 Have one person blow up the balloon until it just fits into the opening of the inflation gauge. Have the same person blow up the balloon every time, and use the inflation gauge so there will be the same amount of air inside.

4 Assemble the balloon and car as shown in the diagram. Set the car on the starting line and let the air rush out of the balloon. Record your observations of how far the car traveled in your ***Activity Log***. Repeat 3 more times and calculate the average distance in your ***Activity Log***.

5 Use a piece of tape to attach a nickel to the top of the jet car. Repeat steps 3 and 4. Does it go as far or as fast? How does the average distance compare with your first trial?

6 Tape another nickel to the car. Repeat steps 3 and 4.

7 Now test the car 4 times with a load of 3 nickels, then 4 times with 4 nickels. Measure the distances the car travels, calculate the average distances, and record them in your *Activity Log*.

What causes this jet car to accelerate?

What Happened?

1. Which accelerated faster—the jet car carrying 4 nickels or the jet car with no extra mass placed on it? Which of these had the greater average distance?
2. Why is it important to use the inflation gauge every time to be sure you blow up the balloon to the same size?

What Now?

1. Would it be possible to get the jet car carrying 4 nickels to accelerate as fast as the jet car that has no extra mass placed on it? How could you do that? Design a new balloon inflation gauge to try this.
2. Two identical pickup trucks are entered in a drag race. The trucks' engines, tires, and bodies are exactly the same, but one of them is carrying a load of bricks in the back. Which truck will probably win the race? Why?

EXPLORE

Why Does Matter Sit Still?
Why Does Matter Keep Moving?

A net force must be applied to both the pebble and the boulder to start them moving.

To answer these questions, let's review your readings and explorations so far. Recall the steeplechase contest and the water balloon race. The motion of the jockey and the motion of water balloons demonstrated a basic property of all matter: Moving matter tends to keep moving in a straight line and at a constant speed unless acted upon by a net force. But what about matter that isn't moving? Is a big lump of matter that is sitting on the ground and not moving (like the big boulder shown in the picture) likely to start moving all by itself? What about a much smaller lump of matter, like the pebble in the girl's hand?

The answer to both questions is no! Matter tends to keep doing what it's already doing. This is true whether the lump is big (like the boulder) or small (like the pebble).

How Is It Possible to Move Matter?

To start matter moving, a net force must be applied to it. Recall from Lesson 2 that a force is a push or a pull that one object exerts on another object. What is a net force? You can experience a net force by doing the Pulling Forces activity below.

TRY THIS Activity!

Pulling Forces

You'll be able to demonstrate a net force using washers in this activity.

What You Need

metal washer, 2 rubber bands, 2 newton spring scales, pencil, paper, goggles, *Activity Log* page 15

Work with a partner. Tie each rubber band to opposite sides of the washer. Attach the spring scales to the free ends of the rubber bands. Place your setup on a sheet of paper on a flat surface. Trace around the washer.

Each person should pull on a spring scale at the same time in opposite directions with the same amount of force (the same number of newtons). *Safety Tip:* Do not pull too hard. Record your observations in your *Activity Log*.

Now each person should pull on a spring scale with a different amount of force, but still in opposite directions. Record your observations in your *Activity Log*.

Balanced forces are equal in size but opposite in direction. When you pulled on the washer the first time, the forces you exerted on it were balanced. The washer won't move from its original position when the forces acting on it are balanced forces.

But what if forces are unbalanced? Unbalanced forces can occur when one force is larger than the other. Unbalanced forces can also occur when one force is not directly opposite the other force. When you pulled on the washer the second time, the forces you exerted on it were unbalanced, and the washer moved.

What will happen if you pull on the washer with equal forces that aren't in opposite directions? Try it.

A **net force** on an object exists when the forces acting on it are unbalanced. A net force will cause an object to start moving, speed up, slow down, stop moving, or change direction. Another way of saying this is that a net force will cause a change in the position of an object or a change in the velocity of an object. Recall that velocity describes both the speed and direction of an object.

Think back to the very beginning of this unit. Remember the tug-of-war contests. In which pictures

on pages 8 and 9 do unbalanced forces exist?

Why Are Some Objects Harder To Move or Harder To Stop Than Others?

Look back at the pictures of the boulder and the pebble in the girl's hand on page 44. Would it be as easy for you to move the giant boulder as it is for the girl to throw the pebble? Why? The pebble and the boulder are both rocks. Can one rock be much harder to move than another? Why are bricks and barbells more resistant to being moved than cotton balls and bananas?

The two dogs pulling on the shoes are pulling with equal and opposite forces. These are balanced forces.

The two dogs pulling on the rope are pulling with unequal but opposite forces. These are unbalanced forces.

Minds On! Let's look at some rules about matter. One example of each rule is given. Work in groups of three to come up with two or three more examples of each rule. List these examples in one person's **Activity Log** page 16, and have all three group members sign the group's work.

1. Moving matter tends to keep moving in a straight line and at a constant speed. (When a horse stops suddenly, its jockey still moves forward.)

2. Matter at rest tends to stay at rest. (Rocks don't move without a push or pull by something.)

3. An unbalanced force or a net force is required to change the speed or direction of moving matter. (Air streaming out of the balloon caused the jet car to move forward. The forces on the jet car were then unbalanced and the jet car began to accelerate.)

4. The more matter an object contains (the more mass it has), the harder it is to change its speed or direction of motion. (A jet car carrying four nickels hardly moves when the balloon's air is released.) ●

n 1686, Sir Isaac Newton combined these different rules about how matter moves into a single statement we now call Newton's First Law of Motion. The First Law of Motion is—

> **An object at rest tends to stay at rest and an object in motion tends to stay in motion in a straight line and at a constant speed, unless acted upon by a net force.**

Newton's statement of the First Law of Motion is also known as the Law of Inertia. **Inertia** (in ûr´ shə) is the property of matter that resists changes in speed or direction of motion. The more mass an object possesses, the more inertia that object possesses, therefore the larger the net force that will be needed to change its velocity. Remember that velocity includes both speed and direction. A change in velocity can be an increase or a decrease.

Inertia is a basic property of all kinds of matter.

From the smallest subatomic particle to the largest galaxy, every speck of matter possesses mass and therefore possesses inertia. The amount of mass each object possesses is a measure of that object's inertia.

In the Jet Racing Cars activity, you saw how more massive objects (the jet car with mass added) had more inertia and did not accelerate (change velocity) as much as the less massive object (the jet car without mass added) did when the same amount of net force was applied. You would have needed to apply a larger net force to the jet car with more mass added to get it to accelerate as much as the jet car with no mass added.

Is this man carrying real boulders or fake boulders?

What Controls How Much Inertia There Is in Matter?

The amount of inertia present in a lump of matter depends partly on size. If you have two barbells made of exactly the same kind of metal, the bigger barbell will have more inertia and be harder to lift.

However, size alone doesn't determine an object's inertia. Look at the picture of the boulder being used in a movie. It looks as if it should have a large amount of inertia and would therefore be very hard to pick up (change its velocity). You've probably already figured out how the man is able to move what you see in the picture with very little force—the boulder is a fake. It's made out of papier-mâché, not granite, as it appears.

The trick boulder shows another important fact about inertia: the amount of inertia that an object possesses depends on both the material the object is made of and the size of the object.

A baseball has more mass than a foam ball of the same diameter; a steel ball the size of a baseball has more mass than both balls. The sizes of the foam ball, baseball, and steel ball are all the same. Their masses are different because the steel ball has more matter in it than the baseball or the foam ball.

Minds On! Have you ever picked up an empty foam ice chest? Only a small amount of net force is needed to change a foam box's velocity from zero (when it is on the ground) to several meters per second.

However, if you fill an empty foam ice chest to the top with ice and soft drinks, it becomes harder to pick up. What will you need to do to pick up a full ice chest? Discuss your answer with your neighbor.●

Sir Isaac Newton developed his ideas about inertia and the laws of motion over a period of years. Read the following pages to learn more about Isaac Newton's work and the way our scientific knowledge changes and is made known.

Sir Isaac Newton

Mo-Tzu

Aristotle

Scientific Development

Have you ever put off writing a report for school until you were forced to do it? That's what Sir Isaac Newton did with his discoveries of the Laws of Motion and the theory of gravitation. Newton completed his research in 1665 when he was only 23 years old. He didn't write a final draft of his findings for 20 years! *Principia Mathematica*, a book describing Newton's findings, wasn't published until 1687!

Newton's work might have been lost had it not been for his astronomer friend, Edmund Halley. Realizing how important Newton's research on motion would be to other scientists, Halley nagged Newton to rewrite his 20-year-old notes. Halley was so intent on having the book published that he paid the printing costs himself.

After Newton's work was published, scientists did experiments to test his conclusions. Their experimental results supported Newton's observations. Older ideas about motion were rejected in view of Newton's findings.

Aristotle's views on motion had been taught in European universities for almost 2,000 years, but his ideas were disproved in light of Newton's findings. Experimental evidence overturned centuries of reliance on the authority of the Greek philosopher. Aristotle believed that a rock thrown horizontally continued moving because air streamed in behind it and forced the rock forward. Scientists testing Aristotle's statement found no evidence of a forward force. Newton's first law, "an object at rest tends to stay at rest and an object in motion tends to stay in motion in a straight line and at a constant speed, unless acted upon by an outside force," replaced Aristotle's thoughts on motion.

But what if Isaac Newton had not published his discoveries? It's quite possible that you would be studying the law of inertia of Mo-Tzu (mô´ tsü´) as well as the law of gravitation of

PHILOSOPHIÆ
NATURALIS
PRINCIPIA
MATHEMATICA.

Autore *JS. NEWTON*, *Trin. Coll. Cantab. Soc.* Matheseos
Professore *Lucasiano*, & Societatis Regalis Sodali.

IMPRIMATUR·
S. P E P Y S, *Reg. Soc.* P R Æ S E S.
Julii 5. 1686.

L O N D I N I,

Jussu *Societatis Regiæ* ac Typis *Josephi Streater.* Prostat apud
plures Bibliopolas. *Anno* MDCLXXXVII.

Principia Mathematica *described Isaac Newton's scientific discoveries.*

Abu 'l Fath Al-Khazini (ä´bü l fäth äl kä zē´ nē). Chinese philosopher Mo-Tzu wrote in the book *Mo Ching:* "The cessation of motion is due to the opposing force...If there is no opposing force...the motion will never stop. This is as true as that an ox is not a horse." This is another way of stating Newton's first law. It was published about 2,000 years before Newton was born.

An 18th century physics book showed this demonstration of Newton's third law of motion.

Scientists are commonly judged both by the quality of their own discoveries and by how those discoveries are used by later generations of scientists. Mo-Tzu is not well-known. Neither is Abu 'l Fath Al-Khazini, an Arabian scientist who stated a law of gravitation 500 years before Newton lived. Their discoveries in physics could have been the starting point for further research but were not, because they weren't published worldwide. That is our loss. Think of how far our knowledge of physics might have advanced by now if the Law of Inertia had been widely known 2,000 years before it was!

Lacking any hint that these discoveries had already been made, Sir Isaac Newton rediscovered the Law of Inertia and revolutionized the science of physics. His work laid the groundwork for the discoveries Albert Einstein made at the beginning of the 20th century. But if Edmund Halley hadn't encouraged him to write up his results, Newton probably wouldn't have received credit for his great scientific insights, any more than Abu 'l Fath Al-Khazini and Mo-Tzu did. What's more, we might still be waiting for someone else to rediscover these physical principles—someone who would find support from a large group of other scientists ready to cooperate in understanding them and furthering the scientific insight they provided. A scientific discovery can be thought of as a lighted candle—if a candle is lighted but no one is using its light to look at something, then the light is being wasted.

Potential and Kinetic Energy

An avalanche is the rapid, sudden fall down a mountain slope of ice, snow, rocks, or mud. Avalanches can be deadly to unlucky skiers. Skiers can start an avalanche by moving across a ledge of snow and applying enough force to crack the layers of snow loose. The resulting avalanche may break trees in half, toss cars off roads, and crush houses.

The ice and snow of an avalanche is pulled down the side of a mountain by the force of gravity. Deep layers of snow and ice that build up on mountains possess a large amount of mass. This mass exerts a huge amount of force on whatever it strikes on its way down the mountain. Avalanches may travel only 20 or 30 meters, or they may roll over mountainsides for more than 2,000 meters (more than a mile).

The snow on this mountain has a great deal of potential energy.

This avalanche has a lot of kinetic energy.

Scientists have a way of describing how much force is being exerted and predicting how much damage that force can do when snow is moving down the mountain. If scientists can estimate the mass and velocity of the snow present in an avalanche, they can calculate its kinetic energy. Kinetic energy is energy of motion. **Kinetic** (ki net´ ik) **energy** is a measure of how much force a moving object exerts as it moves a specific distance. An avalanche of a massive snow pack moving very fast down a steep slope will have a large amount of kinetic energy. The more kinetic energy the avalanche has, the more damage the avalanche can do.

As this mass of snow begins to move downhill, it breaks into blocks.

But geologists want to predict how much damage an avalanche might do before it happens. They can do this by calculating the potential energy of a snow pack. **Potential energy** is energy that an object has due to its position. Potential energy is a measure of how much force an object at rest is capable of exerting if it starts to move.

The amount of potential energy stored in an object depends on two factors: how much mass the object possesses and how high above Earth it is located. A massive, icy layer high on a mountainside has more potential energy than a light, snowy layer on a gentle hillside. The more potential energy the ice has, the more damage it can do if it starts to move.

Geologists and other earth scientists study potential avalanche areas each season. They measure the height of the layer of snow and ice on steep slopes, and they calculate its mass. They can then calculate the potential energy of a snow and ice pack in an avalanche-prone area.

On the basis of their measurements and calculations, earth scientists sometimes deliberately start small avalanches before big, dangerous ones can occur. They do this by setting off explosives where there is danger of a big avalanche.

A well-planned explosion will exert just enough force to break loose the ice crystals that hold the pack of snow and ice in place. In other words, the force of the explosion causes matter at rest (the snow pack) to begin to move. This matter has a great amount of inertia. The net force from the explosion must be very large to overcome the inertia of the snow pack. Once the inertia of the snow pack is overcome, the snow starts to slide downward because of the force of gravity. The moving snow exerts force as it travels down the slope. Another way of saying this is that the potential energy contained by the snow, while it was at rest on top of the mountain, is converted to kinetic energy as it slides downhill during the avalanche.

How Does the First Law of Motion Apply?

This child will continue to move along the water slide until the force of friction slows him down.

You run up to the water slide, leap forward, and slide ten meters across the lawn on your stomach. It's a great way to spend a hot afternoon! You're taking advantage of the First Law of Motion: moving objects continue moving in a straight line and at a constant speed unless acted upon by some unbalanced force. The unbalanced force of friction between your stomach and the water slide will slow you down gently and bring you to a stop.

Coming gently to a stop instead of continuing to move in a straight line can be a matter of life and death at other times. About 40,000 people in the United States die each year in automobile crashes. When a car moving 80 kilometers (about 50 miles) per hour hits a tree, the car crumples and stops moving, but the floor of the car where the seats are attached doesn't stop as quickly as the front bumper. If the passengers are not wearing seat belts, they'll continue to move forward at the same speed, just as the First Law of Motion predicts. They'll stop very suddenly (like the front bumper) when they crash into the dashboard or windshield.

The passengers will come to a less sudden stop if they're wearing seat belts. Seat belts and air bags save lives by applying an unbalanced force to passengers during the time the car crumples, stopping them from continuing in straight-line motion. By holding them in their seats, the seat belts stop the passengers from crashing through the windshield headfirst. Race car drivers using specially designed seat belt systems often walk away unhurt from crashes that occur at over 320 kilometers (about 200 miles) per hour.

Air bags safely prevent drivers and passengers from continuing to move forward at a constant speed in a straight line toward the windshield.

Safer Cars

Air bags and antilock brakes are two new inventions that help drivers and passengers avoid serious injury and death in car crashes. Both of these devices make cars safer by helping to avoid the problems caused by the fact that objects in motion (cars and passengers) tend to travel in a straight line unless acted upon by an outside force. In other words, air bags and antilock braking systems help you deal safely with

Newton's First Law of Motion. Here's how they work. An air bag is a large fabric balloon stored inside the steering column or dashboard of a car. It's connected to collision sensors built into the front of the car and in the passenger compartment. When the sensors detect a change in motion of the car equivalent to the car hitting a brick wall at about 20 kilometers (12 miles) per hour, the sensors send a signal to the air bag. (This speed is about as fast as you can run.) The bag then inflates with nitrogen gas to protect the driver's

and the passenger's heads and chests.

An air bag can be used only once. It inflates in less than 50 milliseconds—about half the time it takes you to blink an eye. It cushions your head and chest and prevents you from hitting any hard surface inside the car. In less than one second after impact, the bag starts to deflate. If it has prevented a car occupant from continuing in straight-line motion (as Newton predicted) and slamming face first into the windshield during an accident, it was a good investment in safety.

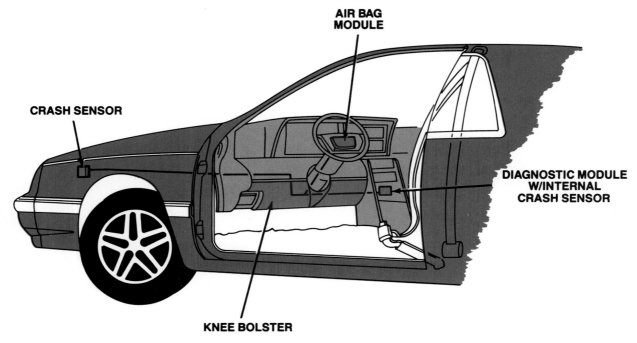

AIR BAG MODULE

CRASH SENSOR

DIAGNOSTIC MODULE W/INTERNAL CRASH SENSOR

KNEE BOLSTER

When the crash sensors detect a large decrease in motion, they send a signal to the air bag to inflate.

Antilock braking systems (ABS) are designed to help drivers avoid having an accident by preventing the car from skidding. Many accidents occur when cars go out of control on wet or icy pavement. If the driver pushes down on the brake pedal too hard in a car with standard brakes, the wheels stop turning and the tires begin to skid.

When a tire is skidding, it can't apply enough force to the road to stop the car quickly or change the direction in which the car is moving. Just as Newton

predicted, a skidding car continues moving in a straight line. If a tree or another car happens to be in the way of that straight line, there is very little the driver of the skidding car can do except hope that the seat belts are secure and the air bag system works.

Cars equipped with ABS are much less likely to skid when the driver applies the brakes during an emergency. The ABS work by having a sensor at each wheel measure how fast the wheel is changing speeds. If the sensor determines that the wheel is about to lock up and cause a skid, a small

computer takes control of the braking system and reduces the pressure being applied to that brake. The wheel doesn't skid, and the driver is still able to steer the car even during an emergency.

Scientists and engineers are working to make cars safer all the time, but no car safety device is perfect. For now, the best advice for any driver or passenger is, "Buckle your lap and shoulder seat belts, and drive carefully." If the car stops suddenly, let the safety belt and the air bag stop your straight-line motion—not the windshield.

When this car drives over the patch of ice, the force of friction between the tires and the road is decreased. The car will begin to skid.

Air bags and seat belts act to control the harmful effects of inertia. But sometimes inertia's effects are exactly what is wanted. Many of the structures that engineers design take advantage of the inertia of certain materials. The more massive an object is, and the more inertia it has, the more it resists being moved. When you want something to stay in place or to hold back a great amount of energy, you make it very massive. Inertia holds earthen dams in place, allowing us to hold water in lakes and control floods. Massive rocks are used to line shipping channels and make jetties. The inertia of the rocks prevents them from being washed away.

Minds On! Work in groups of four to come up with a list of several examples of structures or products that use inertia to hold back force or protect consumers. Write your lists in your **Activity Log** on page 17. Share your list with the other groups in your class. ●

Sum It Up

In this lesson, you've learned that net forces change the state of motion of an object. A net force on an object exists when the forces acting on it are unbalanced—that is, when the forces acting on the object interact in opposite directions with unequal force. Unless an unbalanced or net force acts on an object, the object will tend to keep doing whatever it is already doing. If the object is at rest, it tends to remain at rest. If the object is moving, it tends to continue moving in a straight line and at a constant speed. You've also learned that inertia is the property of matter that resists changes in the speed or direction of motion. More massive objects have more inertia. When you understand how forces act together on matter, you can answer the questions that began this lesson—"Why does matter sit still? Why does matter keep moving?"

Critical Thinking

1. In your own words, tell what Newton's First Law of Motion means.
2. What is the relationship between mass and inertia?
3. Is it possible for an object to have several forces acting on it and still not change its motion? Why or why not?
4. Is it possible for an object to continue to move if there is no force on it in the direction in which it is moving?
5. What do seat belts in cars have to do with the First Law of Motion?

What Controls Acceleration?

—moving faster and faster and faster—

—slowing down more and more and more—

—dodging to the right, darting to the left—

Moving faster, slowing down, and changing directions are all examples of acceleration. Why does a baseball accelerate after it leaves the pitcher's hand? Why does a soccer ball slow down when it hits a fence? In this lesson, you'll explore the kinds of things that affect an object's acceleration.

Propellers roar and tires screech. An airplane and a sports car race side by side down a deserted runway. The car pulls even with the airplane. The fearless hero jumps from the car to the airplane, captures the criminal, and . . . the movie ends.

Could a fast car really catch an airplane before the plane takes off, or is the scene just a movie trick? Is there a scientific way to

compare the speeds of an airplane and a car and predict what will happen? One way to approach this question is to use what you've already learned about measuring an object's motion. In order to figure out if the car can really keep up with the plane, you need to know how far the airplane rolls down the runway and how fast it's moving when it lifts off the ground. In other words, you need to know about the plane's change of position and the plane's acceleration.

Minds On! Can a car accelerate as fast as this airplane? Absolutely! Many sports cars can reach speeds of 160 kilometers (about 100 miles) per hour in 6,000 meters (2,200 feet). Drag-racing cars can accelerate to 400 kilometers (about 250 miles) per hour in 4,000 meters (about 1,465 feet).

By applying your present knowledge of how objects move, can you tell if a chase scene is really happening the way it appears in a movie? ●

Twin-engine airplanes like the one shown need to roll about 6,000 meters (2,200 feet) down the runway in order to reach their takeoff speed of 160 kilometers (about 100 miles) per hour. A car must be able to reach the same speed within the same distance in order for someone to leap from it to the plane.

Activity!

Rolling Along With a Constant Force

Let's explore what causes a change in an object's acceleration.

What You Need

roller skate
string, 1 m
newton spring scale
3 2-L plastic soft-drink
bottles/caps
smooth surface—1 m long
2 L of water
2 L of sand
Activity Log pages 18–19

What To Do

1 Fill a 2-L bottle with water. Leave the second 2-L bottle empty. Fill the third 2-L bottle with sand. Screw the caps on all the bottles.

2 Place the bottle of water on the skate as shown. Attach the skate to the spring scale with a piece of string. Gently pull on the spring scale until you apply just enough force to start the skate and bottle moving very slowly.

3 How many newtons of force did you use to move the bottle of water? Record the data in your *Activity Log.*

4 Remove the bottle of water and place the empty bottle on the skate. Attach the spring scale as before and pull just hard enough to start the skate and empty bottle moving very slowly. Compare the amount of force needed to move the empty bottle to the amount of force needed in step 2. Record your comparison in your *Activity Log.* Leave the empty bottle on the skate. Hold the skate still with one hand. Pull the spring scale until it shows the same amount of force that you used to move the bottle of water in step 2. Keep pulling on the scale with the same amount of force you used to move the bottle of water. Now, let go of the skate. Record your observations in your *Activity Log.*

What Happened?

1. Which has more mass—the empty bottle or the bottle of water?
2. Which takes more force to accelerate—the empty bottle or the bottle of water?
3. When you apply the same amount of force to each bottle, which one accelerates more, the empty bottle or the bottle of water?

What Now?

1. The bottle of sand has more mass and therefore more inertia or resistance to change in motion than either the empty bottle or bottle of water. How much force do you think it would take to accelerate the bottle of sand?
2. Set up an experiment to test your prediction of the amount of force needed to move the bottle of sand. Was your prediction correct?
3. Why do bicycle racers use very low-mass bicycles? Would a bicycle with a large amount of inertia help win a race?

EXPLORE

A Relationship—Pushes and Pulls, Mass, and Acceleration

A large force applied to this soccer ball will cause a large acceleration of the soccer ball.

I n the Explore Activity, you saw that more massive objects require more force to accelerate. The water-filled bottle required more force to accelerate than the empty bottle did. The water-filled bottle had more mass than the empty bottle. The sand-filled bottle had more mass than the water-filled bottle. The sand-filled bottle required more force to accelerate than the water-filled bottle. If you think about it, you experience this relationship every day.

Since we expect matter to move in predictable ways, we plan our actions to suit our predictions about motion. You wouldn't play a game of tennis with a bowling ball or try to knock down a brick wall with a feather.

The force of the foot on this soccer ball causes the ball to accelerate.

A small force applied to this soccer ball will cause a small acceleration of the soccer ball.

Yet feathers and bowling balls are both matter. Recall that all matter is composed of atoms, and atoms are composed of electrons, protons, and neutrons. All matter moves according to the Laws of Motion discovered by Sir Isaac Newton.

Also recall that a force is a push or a pull that one object exerts on another object. Newton's Second Law of Motion states the relationship among pushes and pulls, mass, and acceleration. The Second Law of Motion states—

The acceleration of an object depends on the net force acting on that object and on the mass of that object.

If the mass of an object does not change, the acceleration of the object will increase when a larger force is applied. For example, when you tap a soccer ball with your toe, it hardly moves. Kick it hard, however, and the soccer ball flies down the field.

If the force exerted on two objects is the same, the acceleration of the object with the larger mass will be less than the acceleration of the object with the smaller mass. Race cars are built from very light materials. If two cars are identical except for their masses and the same amount of force is applied by the cars' engines, the race car with the lower mass will accelerate faster than the race car with the greater mass.

When engineers design an automobile, they can use the relationships among mass, force, and acceleration given in Newton's Second Law to predict how the car will perform. During the design stage, engineers may decide to build a car using low-mass or high-mass materials, or they may put a larger engine in the car to produce more force.

An animal, however, doesn't have the option of redesigning itself to improve its ability to accelerate. Once an animal is grown up, its abilities to run, jump, and change direction don't change very much. Yet an animal's speed and mobility can mean the difference between life and death.

Have you ever tried to catch a grasshopper? When a grasshopper sitting on a blade of grass sees you approaching, it uses its big hind legs to spring into the air and fly away. Every time it lands, it uses its hind legs to produce the force required to send it flying off in a different direction.

Grasshopper legs can't produce a large amount of force. But grasshoppers have to be able to escape from bigger, stronger, faster animals including birds, toads, and people. The rela-

This baseball pitcher is exerting a force to accelerate the baseball. The catcher's mitt is well padded to absorb the force of the accelerating baseball.

tionships among a grasshopper's mass, the force it can produce, and its rate of acceleration help to explain how it can avoid being captured.

Grasshoppers are hard to catch because of their

62

great ability to accelerate. They have a small amount of mass, so the small amount of force they can produce with their legs and wings is enough to accelerate them to top speed very quickly. Having low mass also allows grasshoppers to change directions almost instantly. Recall that changing direction while moving is also acceleration.

Many other animals also depend on changing

directions quickly to help assure their survival. Fleas, frogs, and houseflies are all super accelerators. All of them are low in mass, can go from a standstill to top

speed very quickly, and can change directions in a flash. They're living proof that races are not always won by the fastest competitor. Sometimes the best accelerator wins.

Momentum

If you play baseball or hockey, you probably wear a helmet and pads. These protect you if you're hit by the ball or puck. But tennis players don't need to wear pads or a helmet. Tennis balls travel as fast or faster than baseballs, but getting hit by one usually doesn't cause serious injuries. Why do baseballs and hockey pucks hurt when they hit you? You can use Newton's Second Law of Motion to answer this question. First, a baseball has more mass than a tennis ball. Also, changing the speed of a baseball from a large value to zero (or slowing down) requires a large negative acceleration. The force your body must exert to cause this negative acceleration increases as the mass of the

ball increases. The greater force required to stop a baseball compared to a tennis ball is enough to cause severe injury. This is why baseball catchers wear padded catcher's mitts. The padded catcher's mitt absorbs most of the force from the moving baseball. The catcher's hand doesn't need to exert all of the force to slow down and stop the baseball, and the catcher won't experience pain or injury to his or her hand.

But acceleration is hard to measure. Sometimes what you really want to know about a moving object is "Is it going to cause damage if it hits me at that speed?" In other words, how much "bashing power" does it have?

Do the next activity to learn about "bashing power."

This grasshopper uses its hind legs to produce the force that accelerates it forward.

Activity!

Does It Bounce or Does It Bash?

Which do you think has more "bashing power"—a table-tennis ball or a golf ball moving at the same velocity? Do this activity to find out.

What You Need
golf ball, table-tennis ball, large, empty coffee can—open on one end, rubber band, 2 paper tissues, goggles, *Activity Log* page 20

Hold a table-tennis ball in one hand and a golf ball in the other. Hold both balls 1 m above the floor. Release both of them at exactly the same time. They'll hit the floor at the same instant. Are they traveling at the same speed when they hit the floor? How can you tell?

Place a paper tissue on top of the open end of a large, empty can. Hold it in place with the rubber band so that it's tight like a drumhead. Hold the table-tennis ball 1 m above the can and drop it so that the ball hits the middle of the tissue. (If the ball doesn't hit the center of the tissue, try again.) What happens?

Place a new paper tissue on top of the open end of the can as you did before. Hold the golf ball 1 m above the can and drop it so the ball hits the middle of the tissue. (If the ball doesn't hit the center of the tissue, try again.) What happens this time? Which ball has more "bashing power?" Record your answers in your *Activity Log.*

"Bashing Power" is Momentum!

Scientists have a term that means "bashing power." They call it momentum. **Momentum** (mō men' təm) is defined as the product of an object's velocity times its mass. You probably already know that getting hit by a massive object (like a car) or getting hit by a fast-moving object (like a baseball) will hurt. An object's "bashing power" depends on its mass times its velocity, or its momentum. Think about momentum as you debate about bicycle helmet laws on page 65.

Momentum is defined as the product of an object's velocity times its mass.

A bicycle safety helmet protects its wearer's head from injury in the event of an accident.

SCIENCE
TECHNOLOGY
AND Society

Bicycle Helmet Laws

How much momentum do you have as you ride a bicycle down the street? Your mass doesn't change as you ride along, but often your velocity increases (you accelerate). As your velocity increases, your momentum increases—you have more "bashing power."

What happens if you fall from your bicycle with this greater "bashing power?" You would probably injure yourself! Approximately 1,000 Americans die each year as a result of bicycle accidents. The cause of death is head trauma in 75 percent of these accidents.

Lawmakers in some areas of the United States have passed bills requiring all bicyclists to wear helmets or pay fines—as much as $100 per violation. The makers of these laws realize that the greater "bashing power" a bicycle rider's head has, the greater the risk of injury to the head.

Many bicycle riders don't want to wear helmets. They think helmets are hot and uncomfortable. These "anti-helmet" bicycle riders feel that laws shouldn't require them to wear safety helmets if they don't want to.

What do you think? Get together with several of your classmates who have different opinions on bicycle helmet laws. Have a debate about the pros and cons of bicycle safety helmet laws.

The Momentum of Space Junk

Would you believe that a piece of aluminum the size of a pencil eraser could cause as much damage to an orbiting space shuttle as a bomb? It's true! Over a million tiny pieces of "space trash" consisting of flecks of paint, plastic, and small pieces of metal from old satellites are orbiting Earth at very high velocities. Many pieces are in orbits where they may hit the space shuttle or other satellites. The momentum of this trash is so large that space scientists and astronauts are worried about the potential danger it poses.

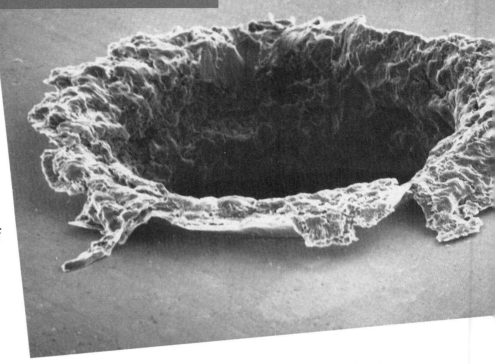

This is a scanning electron micrograph of a crater in the louvers of a space satellite. The satellite had been exposed to space for about 50 months. Scientists found six holes per square foot of the louvers. These craters were caused by very high velocity impacts with paint flakes.

Pieces of space trash in orbit may hit orbiting satellites like this one.

Most of the pieces of space trash are very small— no bigger than this letter "*o.*" But these small pieces of junk are moving at extremely high velocities— about 11,200 meters (about 7 miles) per second. These objects have a small mass, but because of the high velocities at which they are moving, they have an enormous amount of momentum.

In 1983, the windshield of a space shuttle was hit by a fleck of paint smaller than the dot over this letter "*i.*" This paint particle gouged a small crater in the window. If the window had broken, the spacecraft might have been destroyed during reentry.

The National Aeronautics and Space Administration (NASA) is concerned about the dangers caused by space trash. NASA is sponsoring research on ways to avoid damage caused by these tiny bits of orbiting junk. Someday we may launch a space-traveling, garbage-collecting satellite to make space travel safer!

Literature Link

Burton's Zoom Zoom Va-ROOOM Machine

How do people come up with ideas such as a space-traveling, garbage-collecting satellites? Usually ideas such as this come from a need that someone has identified.

"Where do ideas come from, anyway? Burton didn't know. They just happened.

Sometimes he saw a problem that cried out for an answer, like poor Clinton's misery. That had resulted in the Automatic Dog-Washing Machine.

Sometimes he just wished things didn't have to be the way they were— like having to make his bed every morning. And so his No-Hands Automatic BedMaking Machine came to be.

Sometimes his ideas grew out of things he seemed to see in snow swirling in the wind or in the shadowy lines of a tree.

There were more ideas around than Burton could possibly use. It was only when he saw a really great one that he glommed onto it and set to work. He worked fast, never able to catch up with his excitement.

There was no way Burton could have guessed the astonishing idea that was waiting for him to find it that particular day." (excerpted from *Burton's Zoom Zoom Va-ROOOM Machine* by Dorothy Haas)

Have you ever invented anything? Whether you have or not, where do you think ideas come from? Brainstorm with one or two classmates to decide on a problem that needs a solution. Then come up with several ideas to solve it. The ideas don't have to be practical or even possible. Just make them creative.

Applying the Second Law of Motion

How has Newton's Second Law of Motion changed the way we live? Let's look at some more creative ideas in the fields of medical and sports engineering.

R oger jogged three kilometers this afternoon. Lots of people do that, but Roger does it while wearing two artificial legs made of carbon fiber, the space-age metal titanium (tī tā' nē əm), and a new type of plastic. These strong, low-mass materials of which his artificial legs are made have helped Roger lead a much more active life.

Roger's legs were badly injured in a car crash. It was necessary to amputate them. He was fitted with a pair of wooden legs and learned to walk again. But the wooden legs were heavy. After walking a few blocks, he would need to rest. The Second Law of Motion helps explain why Roger's new legs are so much easier to use than the more massive older set.

Roger's use of low-mass artificial legs has allowed him to accelerate faster than when he used heavier wooden artificial legs.

When you are walking or running, the muscles of your thighs and hips apply a force to your lower legs. This causes your lower legs and feet to accelerate. The more massive your foot and lower leg is, the more force is required to move them forward quickly.

Roger's thigh and hip muscles can produce only a limited amount of force. When these muscles are applying their maximum force to a large mass, they get tired quickly. By switching to artificial legs made of less massive materials, Roger was able to reduce the mass that his muscles had to accelerate with each step. Using low-mass artificial legs allowed Roger to accelerate faster than when he used the heavier wooden legs with the same maximum amount of force.

Reducing the mass of sports equipment can also improve other athletes' performances. Imagine how hard it would be to run a 10-kilometer (6.2-mile) race with a brick strapped to each of your shoes! Competitive runners wear low-mass racing shoes for the same reason that Roger benefitted from low-mass artificial legs.

Runners can accelerate more quickly in low-mass shoes. In a long race, low-mass shoes are less tiring to wear. Running shoes need to provide a balance between low mass and adequate protection for the runners' feet, however. Sports shoes are designed to protect the runner's feet from injuries and to spring off the running surface, allowing the runner to bounce a little on each stride. If the mass is too low, foot protection is sacrificed.

Looking Back

Remember the race between the airplane and the sports car? The sports car accelerated at about the same rate as the airplane. Now can you use the Second Law of Motion to explain how they accelerated at about the same rate?

Sum It Up

In this lesson, you've been studying Newton's Second Law of Motion and learning how forces, mass, and acceleration act in relationship to each other. Newton's Second Law of Motion states that the acceleration of an object depends on the force applied to it and on the mass of the object. You've seen Newton's Second Law at work when you exerted a force to accelerate a roller skate with different amounts of mass on it. You've also studied the relationship among force, mass, and acceleration in the real world—in cars and planes, in sports, and in insects and other animals jumping to save their lives. Momentum is the product of mass times velocity. Momentum can be thought of as "bashing power." You experienced the effects of mass times velocity or "bashing power" when you dropped a golf ball and a table-tennis ball

onto a paper tissue. The harmful interactions that take place when one massive object hits another can be prevented or reduced by the use of helmets, seat belts, and air bags. Whether the forces, masses, and accelerations that are acting together on an object are great or small, Newton's Second Law always governs what happens.

Critical Thinking

1. In your own words, explain Newton's Second Law of Motion.
2. Why do some sports cars accelerate quickly?
3. If a tennis ball and a baseball are moving at the same velocity, which has more momentum? Why?
4. A baseball player found that she could hit the ball farther when she used a heavier bat. However, when she tried an even heavier bat, she didn't hit the ball as far. Why do you think this happened?
5. Why does it take more force to pedal a bicycle to get it started moving than when you are already bicycling along a level street?

What Are Action and Reaction Forces?

Action and reaction pairs. What do these words have to do with forces? What interaction occurs between two objects that causes an action and a reaction? If you push your hand against the wall, does the wall push back against your hand? In this lesson, you'll explore how forces always exist in action and reaction pairs.

Struggling to control the fire hose, a team of firefighters advances toward a solid wall of flames. The fire and smoke are dangerous, but so is the force exerted by the fire hose. No single firefighter is strong enough to control the force exerted by this large fire hose. The hose pushes backward against the firefighters. They must work as a team to push the hose forward toward the fire. If the wiggling hose escapes their grasp, it may whip around and seriously injure a member of the team.

Dangling over the edge of a cliff, a rock climber's safety depends on her climbing skill and on the rope to which she is attached. The upward force exerted on the climber by the rope is saving her from falling. Climbers inspect their ropes carefully before each use. What might happen if a sharp rock sliced partway through the rope? Do the next activity to look at action and reaction forces.

The firefighters must work as a team to push the hose toward the fire.

Activity!

Wheeling Away!

Let's experience pairs of forces.

What You Need

desk chair on wheels, 2–L plastic bottle, sand, *Activity Log* page 21

Sit on the desk chair and push against the wall with your foot. Did you and the chair change positions? How far did you travel? In what direction did you move? Can you name the pairs of forces?

Return the chair to its original position, and this time push harder against the wall. When you push against the wall, do you feel the wall pushing back against your foot? Now move the chair away from the wall. Clear a large space in front of and behind the chair. Fill the 2–L bottle with sand. Sit in the chair with both feet a few inches off the floor and hold the sand-filled bottle in front of your chest. Using both hands, push the bottle away from your body and release it.

Safety Tip: Be sure no one is close enough to be hit by the bottle!

How did you apply a force to the bottle? Did the bottle apply a force to you? Did the chair move when you released the bottle? Record your observations in your ***Activity Log***.

Minds On! Have you ever filled a balloon with air and let it go? What happened? Does it take a force to fill a balloon with air? How can you tell? Does the air inside a balloon exert a force against the rubber sides of the balloon? How can you tell? Do the rubber sides of the balloon exert a force against the air inside? How can you tell? Why does the balloon fly around the room when you let go of the open end? What forces are acting on the balloon and on the air? ●

According to Sir Isaac Newton, seeing an apple falling from a tree stimulated his thinking and led to his discovering what we now call Newton's Laws of Motion.

You already know about Newton's First and Second Laws. These laws explain how unbalanced forces affect the motion of matter. Now you'll explore Newton's Third Law of Motion.

This climber exerts a downward force on the rope.

Activity!

Launching a Balloon-Powered Rocket

Let's build and test a rocket that uses a balloon for its engine.

What You Need

balloon
long thin plastic bag
plastic drinking straw
4 m of string
masking tape (2 pieces, each
   about 8 cm long)
meterstick
Activity Log pages 22–23

What To Do

1 Tie one end of the string to the back of a chair or desk. Push the string through the drinking straw. Tie the other end of the string to a second chair. Move the chairs apart until the string is level and tight.

2 Tape the plastic bag to the straw as shown. Blow up the balloon and hold the end closed. Don't tie a knot in the end!

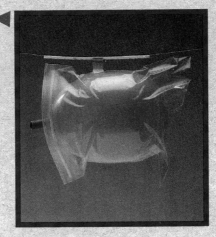

3 Pull the straw and plastic bag to one end of the string so that the open end of the plastic bag is at the knot in the string. Place the balloon inside the plastic bag and let go. What do you observe? Use the meterstick to measure the distance traveled.

4 Have the same student blow up the balloon again. Place the balloon inside the plastic bag and fly the balloon-powered rocket along the string again. Repeat this process 4 more times. Measure the distances traveled with the meterstick. Record your measurements and observations in your *Activity Log.* Calculate the average distance traveled.

What Happened?

1. How far did the balloon rocket travel along the string? What was the average distance traveled by the balloon rocket?
2. What pushes the air out of the balloon? Would the straw travel along the string if you attached a paper bag full of air to the straw and then let go? Why or why not?
3. What do you think caused your balloon-powered rocket to move in the direction it did?

What Now?

1. How can you measure the average speed of the balloon?
2. Help your teacher organize a balloon rocket race. How could you make your balloon-powered rocket go faster? Can you make it travel completely across the room?

EXPLORE

73

Equal and Opposite Forces

Newton asked himself, "Where do forces come from?" He realized that forces always come in pairs that are equal and act in opposite directions. The apple he may have seen hanging from a tree was pulling down against the limb of the tree. The limb, on the other hand, was pulling up against the weight of the apple. These upward and downward forces were opposite and equal. Newton decided that a force applied to any object must be applied by another object. Newton was able to then state his Third Law of Motion—

Whenever an object exerts a force on a second object, the second object exerts an equal and opposite force on the first object.

The force of the expanding gases escaping through the nozzle of the rocket is the action force.

Gases expanding

Nozzle opens ; expanding gases escape

This law can be stated in terms of action and reaction forces—**for every action force, there is an equal but opposite reaction force.** It's important to note that the "action" force and the "reaction" force are acting on different objects.

Both balloon-powered rockets and rockets traveling in outer space provide good examples of equal and opposite action-reaction forces. The stretched balloon pushes on the air, forcing it out of the open end of the balloon. This is the action force. An equal and opposite reaction force occurs inside the balloon as the air pushes back on the balloon. This reaction force pushes the straw forward along the fishing line.

Rocket boosters attached to the space shuttle push it into orbit in the same way. When the space shuttle's rocket boosters are started, they burn fuel and produce large amounts of hot gases that rush out of the back of the booster. That's the action force. The reaction force of the gases pushing back on the booster is equal in strength but opposite in direction. This reaction force sends the shuttle and rocket boosters upward.

Let's look back to some of the examples given in the first part of this lesson and see how the Third Law of Motion explains what's happening.

Remember the fire hose shooting water on the burning building. The nozzle of the fire hose is pushing in the opposite direction from which the water is moving. The water pushing against the nozzle produces an action force. The nozzle pushing back against the water produces the reaction force. The reaction force is exactly equal in strength but pointed in the opposite direction of the force of the hose. Firefighters are able to hold the nozzle still by pushing it toward the building with all their strength.

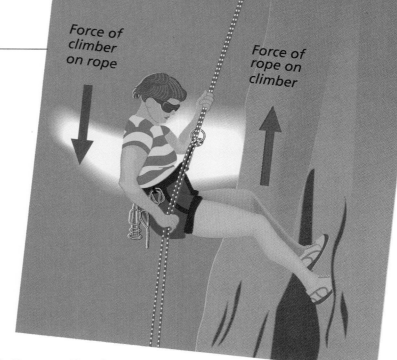

Action-reaction forces

They're using their muscles to produce a force that balances the reaction force. As long as the forces are balanced, the net force on the hose is zero, and the nozzle doesn't move.

Pairs of action and reaction forces are present whether matter is moving or sitting still. Forces always act in pairs. Look back at the picture on page 71 showing the rock climber dangling in mid-air. She isn't moving up or down. She is exerting a downward action force on the rope equal to the weight of her body and equipment. The rope is exerting an upward reaction force on the climber. The upward force of the rope on the climber is exactly equal to the downward force exerted by the climber on the rope. However, until an unbalanced force acts on the climber, she will not move up or down.

Action-reaction forces

Mollusk Movers

Action and reaction forces are found in nature as well. Mollusks make up the largest group of water animals. Mollusks are generally slow moving creatures like snails, slugs, scallops, squids, and clams. But several types of mollusks use very specialized action-reaction forces to move around quite rapidly.

Scallops are two-shelled mollusks that look similar to clams. Scallops can change their locations or escape danger by rapidly opening and closing their shells. When a scallop closes its shells, water is forced out from between the shells. The action force is caused by the force of the shells on the water. The scallop then shoots backward. This reaction is caused by the force of the expelled water on the scallop's shells.

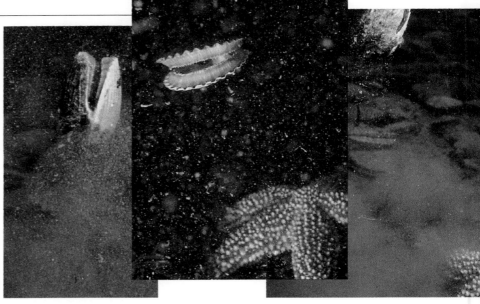

This scallop is using action and reaction forces to escape from the sea star, a predator.

Squids are another type of mollusk that use an even more remarkable scheme for high- speed swimming. Squids are fast-moving hunters that live in the sea. They use their tentacles to swim forward or backward and to grasp the fish they eat. But if a squid is trying to catch a fish to eat (or avoid being eaten by a much bigger fish), it shoots a high-velocity stream of water out of a tube in its body (the action force). The reaction force is caused by the force of the expelled water on the squid. The result of this reaction force is acceleration in the direction opposite to the high-velocity stream of water. Can you see a similarity between the squid and the fire hose?

Squids use action-reaction forces to accelerate rapidly. The funnel tube can be reversed for acceleration in the opposite direction.

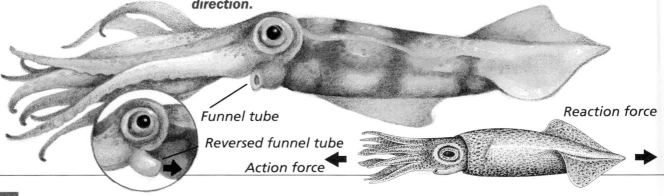

Funnel tube

Reversed funnel tube

Action force

Reaction force

Health 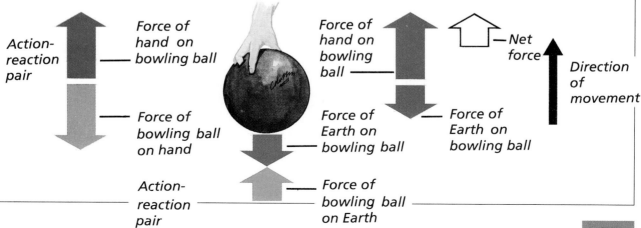 Link

If You Provide the Action, What's the Reaction?

All sporting events involve action and reaction forces. Some are very obvious, and some are a bit harder to identify. For example, when you're roller skating and you push against the wall, you're exerting an action force on the wall. The wall exerts an equal and opposite reaction force on you that will accelerate you away from the wall. You can't see the wall moving in the opposite direction, but there is a very small motion of the area of the wall that you pushed against. Another example would be hitting a baseball. You exert an action force with the bat on the ball, but the ball also exerts an equal and opposite reaction force on the bat.

Work in groups of three or four to list as many action-reaction forces in sporting events as you can. Record these sporting

What are the action and reaction forces in these sporting events?

events in your **Activity Log** page 24. Trade lists with other groups and discuss these sporting events in class. Remember—action-reaction forces act on different objects!

Each of the action-reaction pairs shown is equal. The net force on the bowling ball is in the upward direction, therefore the bowling ball is accelerated upward.

Action-reaction pair —— Force of hand on bowling ball

—— Force of bowling ball on hand

Force of hand on bowling ball ——

Force of Earth on bowling ball

—Net force

Force of Earth on bowling ball

Direction of movement

Action-reaction pair —— Force of bowling ball on Earth

77

Why Do We Need To Know About the Third Law of Motion?

The Third Law of Motion can help you predict what will happen when you apply a force to an object. This happens daily in your life. For instance, when you push the door to your classroom open, the door will exert a force on your hand. That's why it takes some work to push the door open. You need to overcome the force the door exerts on your hand.

The Third Law of Motion is also important for many technical jobs, such as engineering, architecture, and mechanics. People who work in these fields need to know about action and reaction forces so they can plan how to control all possible forces when doing their jobs.

How does knowing about Newton's Third Law of Motion aid a bridge designer? Do the following activity to find out.

TRY THIS Activity!

Design Your Own Bridge!

Use your knowledge of action and reaction forces to build a model bridge from playing cards.

What You Need
deck of playing cards, masking tape

Work with 2 other students to build a support structure for a bridge that is strong enough to support 2 large textbooks, using only playing cards and masking tape. Rules for building your bridge: You may use no more than 10 playing cards to construct your bridge. You can't use any wood, steel, or other sturdy material to make your bridge stronger. You may use masking tape to hold the structure together.

How you construct the bridge is completely up to your design team. Be creative! Experiment with your design and build something original! Whose bridge will be the strongest? Who will have the most unique design? Which team will use the fewest playing cards to hold up the books? Build yours and find out!

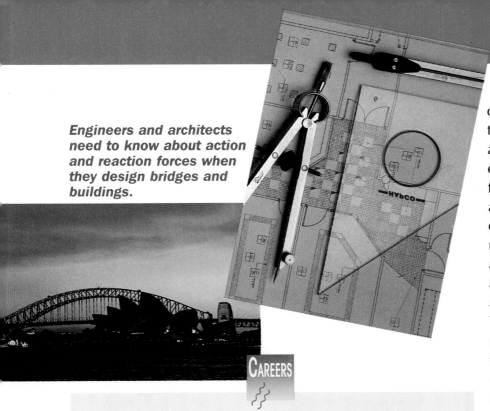

Engineers and architects need to know about action and reaction forces when they design bridges and buildings.

CAREERS

Structural Design Engineers

The Third Law of Motion is very important to structural design engineers. Part of the job of structural design engineers is to design frameworks and foundations for buildings and equipment. If these engineers didn't understand applications of the Third Law of Motion, many engineering decisions would be a matter of guesswork.

To become a structural design engineer, you must study mathematics, physics, and engineering in college.

Having a curiosity about forces and motion helps! Part of the job of structural design engineers is to study what causes structural failures of equipment. The engineers then work out solutions to prevent future breakdowns. Good engineering designs make buildings and equipment safer and more reliable to use. With their knowledge and experience, structural design engineers really make a difference in people's lives!

of action forces and reaction forces—"For every action force, there is an equal and opposite reaction force." Remember, action and reaction forces act on different objects. You experienced these forces interacting on matter in your activity with the balloon and straw on a string. You've also explored and read about action and reaction forces in sporting events, space travel, and underwater life. In fact, no two objects anywhere can interact without there being action and reaction forces.

Critical Thinking

1. In your own words, explain Newton's Third Law of Motion.
2. A girl climbs a rope during gym class. She exerts a force on the rope due to her weight. What other force or forces are involved in this situation?
3. What action and reaction pairs exist when catching a basketball?
4. What action and reaction pairs exist when sleeping in a bed?
5. What action and reaction pairs exist when a rocket accelerates into space?

Sum It Up

Newton's Third Law of Motion says, "For every force, there is an equal and opposite force." This law can also be stated in terms

Tug-of-War Contests Revisited

Do you recall the tug-of-war contests shown at the beginning of this unit? Let's apply what we've learned throughout this unit to see who will really win these contests!

Is the force exerted on the rope by the team on the left balanced by the force exerted on the rope by the team on the right? What will have to happen in order for one of the teams to win this tug-of-war contest?

Is the force exerted on the rope by the adult balanced by the force exerted on the rope by the children? What will have to happen for a winner to be declared in this tug-of-war contest?

Is the force exerted on the rope by the children balanced by the force exerted on the rope by the boulder? How could the children win this tug-of-war contest?

Is the force exerted on the rope by the children on roller skates balanced by the force exerted on the rope by the children in shoes? What will happen when both teams exert more force on the rope?

Environmental Costs

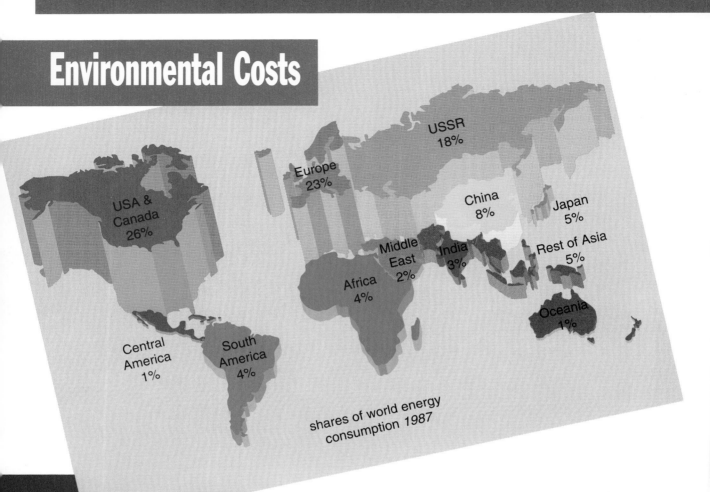

USA & Canada 26%

Europe 23%

USSR 18%

China 8%

Japan 5%

Middle East 2%

India 3%

Rest of Asia 5%

Africa 4%

Oceania 1%

Central America 1%

South America 4%

shares of world energy consumption 1987

Burning coal produces energy that can be used to produce force. The environmental cost is air pollution.

You've looked at the forces involved in tug-of-war contests, and you've identified where these forces were working and how they interacted with each other and with matter. Now, let's think about other places where forces are important and how they are produced.

Today in the United States, we often use machines to produce the force needed to get us from one place to another or to process the food we eat. The machines use energy in the form of coal, oil, and gas to produce the force. Before many of these machines were invented, however, people used to rely on muscle power to do some of these jobs. Some countries still rely on older forms of producing force.

These countries use much less of the world's limited fossil-fuel resources to support each person. An average resident of India uses about 50 times less energy than is used by a United States resident.

What are the environmental costs of using so much energy? The costs include air pollution, oil spills, decreasing amounts of ozone in the atmosphere, decreasing numbers of forests on Earth...the list of environmental concerns is long.

Some of the solutions to these concerns lie in making informed decisions about the methods we use to produce force and do work. If you can use your muscles to walk to the library, should you ask someone to drive you there? If a system of mass transportation could be developed in your area, would enough people ride it instead of driving their cars? Walking or riding mass transportation helps to conserve fuel and thereby stretch Earth's limited fuel reserves.

Work with two friends to do the following Try This Activity. How can you use your knowledge of forces to help make a difference in the world?

TRY THIS Activity!

A New Way To Move

Work in groups of 3 to design a new method of transportation. This could be a new type of bicycle, a new type of car, a new type of boat, or whatever you decide. Try to make your new method of transportation use energy efficiently. Brainstorm to come up with several ideas, then choose the best idea and test it. Use what you now know about forces—frictional forces, gravitational forces, balanced and unbalanced forces, and action and reaction forces—to help with your design. Share responsibility for gathering background information and equipment, then work together to build your transportation model. Share your model with your classmates.

GLOSSARY

Use the pronunciation key below to help you decode, or read, the pronunciations.

Pronunciation Key

a	at, bad	d	dear, soda, bad
ā	ape, pain, day, break	f	five, defend, leaf, off, cough, elephant
ä	father, car, heart	g	game, ago, fog, egg
âr	care, pair, bear, their, where	h	hat, ahead
e	end, pet, said, heaven, friend	hw	white, whether, which
ē	equal, me, feet, team, piece, key	j	joke, enjoy, gem, page, edge
i	it, big, English, hymn	k	kite, bakery, seek, tack, cat
ī	ice, fine, lie, my	l	lid, sailor, feel, ball, allow
îr	ear, deer, here, pierce	m	man, family, dream
o	odd, hot, watch	n	not, final, pan, knife
ō	old, oat, toe, low	ng	long, singer, pink
ô	coffee, all, taught, law, fought	p	pail, repair, soap, happy
ôr	order, fork, horse, story, pour	r	ride, parent, wear, more, marry
oi	oil, toy	s	sit, aside, pets, cent, pass
ou	out, now	sh	shoe, washer, fish mission, nation
u	up, mud, love, double	t	tag, pretend, fat, button, dressed
ū	use, mule, cue, feud, few	th	thin, panther, both
ü	rule, true, food	<u>th</u>	this, mother, smooth
ù	put, wood, should	v	very, favor, wave
ûr	burn, hurry, term, bird, word, courage	w	wet, weather, reward
ə	about, taken, pencil, lemon, circus	y	yes, onion
b	bat, above, job	z	zoo, lazy, jazz, rose, dogs, houses
ch	chin, such, match	zh	vision, treasure, seizure

acceleration (ak sel´ ə rā´ shən): the rate at which velocity changes

action-reaction pairs (ak´ shən-re ak´ shən): two forces, acting on different bodies, having equal strength but opposite direction

air resistance (âr re zis´ təns): the force of air against a moving object; also called drag

average speed (av´ rij spēd): the total distance an object travels divided by the total time it takes to travel the distance

balanced forces (bal´ ənsed fôrs ez): forces, acting on the same body, equal in size but opposite in direction

constant speed (kon´ stənt spēd): no change in speed; acceleration is zero

drag: see air resistance

force: a push or pull one body exerts on another

friction (frik´ shən): a force that opposes motion between two surfaces that are touching each other

gravity (grav´ i tē): the mutual force of attraction that exists between all objects in the universe, force Earth exerts on all objects on or near it

hypothesis (hī poth´ ə sis): the proposed answer to a question or tentative solution to a problem; an educated guess based on observation

inertia (in ûr´ shə): the property of a body that resists any change in velocity

kinetic energy (ki net´ ik en´ ər jē): energy of motion; a measure of how much force a moving object exerts as it moves a specific distance

magnet: any object that has a magnetic field and is able to exert forces on other magnets

mass: the amount of matter in an object; the measure of the inertia of a body

matter: anything that has mass and takes up space

momentum (mō men´ təm): the mass of an object multiplied by its velocity

motion (mō´ shən): change in position

negative acceleration (neg´ ə tiv ak sell ə rā´ shən): a decrease in the rate of velocity

net force (net fôrs): force that results from unbalanced forces acting on an object; changes the motion of an object

newton (N) (nū´ tən): the unit of force; force required to accelerate a 1-kg mass at the rate 1 m/s/s

physicists (fiz´ ə sists): scientists who study the structure and interaction of matter, as well as the changes in position that matter undergoes

plates: rigid blocks of Earth's crust and upper mantle

potential energy (pə ten´ sh l): the energy due to position or condition; a measure of how much force an object at rest is capable of exerting if it starts to move

spring scale (spring skāl): a device used to measure force in newtons

total distance: the maximum time it takes to travel a certain distance

total time: the maximum separation of two positions

unbalanced forces (un bal ənsed fôrs ez): forces, acting on the same body, unequal in size and/or opposite in direction

velocity (və los´ i tē): the speed and direction of a moving object

weight: the force of gravity that Earth exerts on an object resting on its surface

INDEX

INDEX continued

CREDITS